WESTSIDE BARBELL
The Conjugate System Enhanced Through the Research of Westside Barbell

By Louie Simmons
Westside4Athletes®

Published by Westside4Athletes®
Made in the United States of America.

www.westside-barbell.com
Email: customercare@westside-barbell.com

Cover credit: Charlie Cataline

Photographer credit: Harold Sharp

Editors: Martha Johnson and Doris Simmons

Page Design: Justin Oefelein

ISBN-13: 978-0-9973925-9-3

TABLE OF CONTENTS

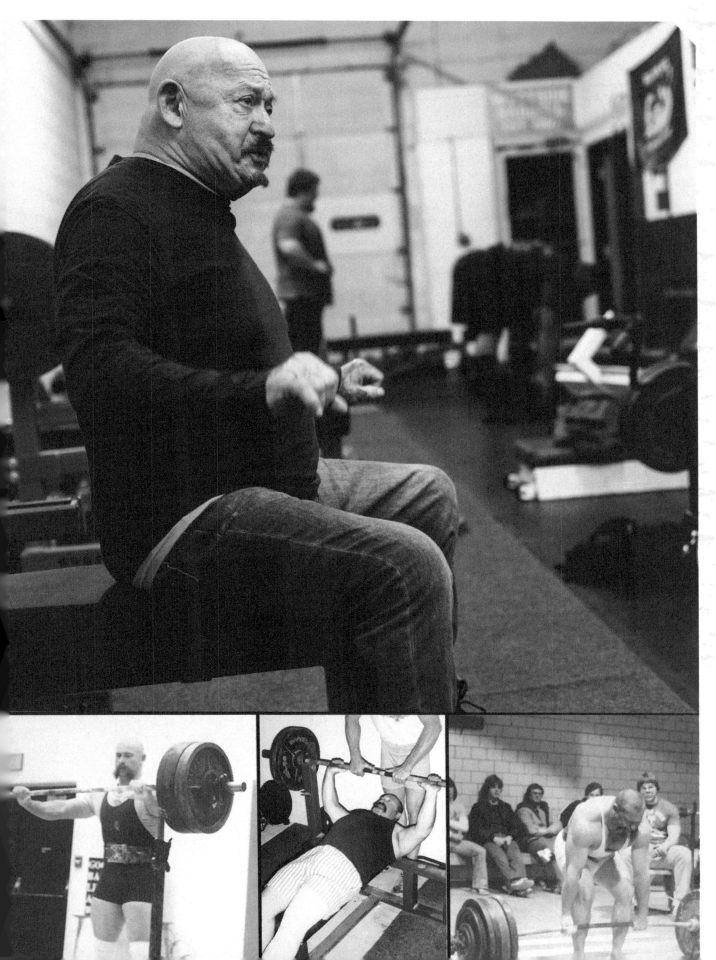

ABOUT THE AUTHOR

Louie Simmons owns Westside Barbell, the strongest powerlifting gym globally with 140 all-time world records. He founded the enterprise in 1986. He is one of only four men to Total Elite in five weight classes with two-hour weigh-ins ranging from the 181-pound class to the 275-pound class. Louie earned a Top Ten ranking for 34 years from 1971 to 2005.

Louie is known for three-week wave periodization. He also is credited with establishing Combinations of Resistance Methods using bands and chains in conjunction with the barbell, contrast methods, and plyometrics while utilizing the Conjugate System.

The owner of twelve patents, he has authored thirteen books on special strength training. In recognition of Louie's methodologies and general contributions to the development of special strength training, he is the 2021 recipient of the National Strength and Conditioning Association (NSCA) Alvin Roy Award. Alvin Roy helped establish strength and conditioning as the cornerstone of any training program, was one of the first coaches to show that lifting weights would improve both speed and power, and helped debunk the myth that lifting weights made athletes slower. In Roy's honor, this esteemed award has been given since 1986 to an individual whose career achievements substantially impacted the scientific understanding, methodologies, and practice of resistance training as a component of sports conditioning.

"Don't train maximally,
never train minimally,
always train OPTIMALLY."
—Louie Simmons

THE CONJUGATE SYSTEM

Like many gyms, Westside Barbell has been using the conjugate system since before 1970 based on training articles written by Westside, Culver City, California, lifters. The recommendations had this reader/author switching special barbell exercises each workout on what is known today as Maximum Effort, or M-E Day. One day was designated for squat and deadlift, and pressing had its own day. Other workouts used a Western Periodization Program. The intensity and volume would change each week, but it went unnoticed.

I believed then that there must be a more sophisticated program, but where would I find it? The answer turned out to be the Soviet Union.

THE BIRTH
OF THE CONJUGATE SYSTEM

In 1972 Y.V. Verkhoshansky and A. N. Medvedev devised a training system that included all special sports training methods. They introduced it at the world-famous Dynamo Club in the former Soviet Union.

For weight lifting, they used 70 high-skilled, master-of-sport-rated weightlifters to review the system. Instead of the standard press snatch and clean and jerk, they presented 25 to 40 special exercises to enhance the classical lifts for 12 weeks.

After the experiment, now known as the Conjugate System, one lifter was satisfied. Still, the other lifters requested more workouts and exercise varieties.

It took another ten years before the name Conjugate System was known to the West. It became known to the West primarily because of the Columbus, Ohio, Westside Barbell Club, and my own work promoting its usage.

The Conjugate System can be confusing to many, and it also can be completely misunderstood. Let's look at football, baseball, and boxing to develop a better understanding.

Football

In football, there are many different offensive plays. Players must interact and work together from play to play to be successful and build momentum. You might have a running play then a pass play. It becomes a complex problem to solve for the defense. That would include trick plays, punts, and attempting a field goal. Also, there is the need to decide whether to switch players or slow or speed up the count. The defense has many options to stop the forward progress of the offense with many defense formations. The offense, however, will adjust to the defense to gain a first down, score from a field goal, or a touchdown.

Now, let's look at baseball.

Baseball

First, the offense will give their lineup for the hitters, and where each player will play defense—second base or maybe right field, for example.

Next, the pitcher will take signs from the catcher for what he will throw. It could be a fastball or a curveball, or it may be a change-up. By mixing the pitches, they hope to confuse the batter into striking out or keeping the ball in play.

Simultaneously, the hitter is trying to hit the ball safely to get onto a base. The coach will exchange players for hitting or running a base or change a right-hander for a left-hander.

Suppose you look at the sidelines for both sports. A coach gives the team or a particular player signals, like the pitcher in baseball or the quarterback in football.

Everything is constantly changing but connected.

Boxing

To be a master boxer, you must first learn the basics. That includes boxing skills as well as general physical preparedness (GPP), also known as conditioning.

After the boxer is well prepared to compete, he uses different combinations of moves against his rival. Actions include advanced footwork, keeping the correct distance, and traps set up many times with feints with your feet, hands, or head.

Shaun O'Grady, a former world champion at lightweight boxing, once said, "when you really learn to box, you are too old to box."

He was right. There is so much to learn about boxing before the parts become a whole. Every aspect of the art of boxing blends together when the boxer is fighting.

UNDERSTANDING
THE CONJUGATE SYSTEM

Generally, all sports are similar to the Conjugate System when rotating personnel or switching plays, or even controlling the clock for proper time management. To be successful at a high level, all sports athletes must make changes during the competition. A golf pro will interchange different clubs during a match. Still, this flexibility is just one element of the Conjugate System. In *Supertraining*, Verkhoshansky explains it as teaching the basic motor system that could hold back improvement of specific motor ability.

The Conjugate System of Training Methods

The Conjugate System makes it possible to train all aspects of athletic movements. It can be rotating large and small exercises, volume, intensities, velocities, or GPP aerobic and anaerobic capabilities.

It also covers all special strengths and special endurances while the coach and athlete can work on sports-specific preparation (SSP) while improving the cardiovascular system. One of the most significant benefits is avoiding the Law of Accommodation. The athlete experiences a decrease in all manner of training when he or she trains with the same load of volume. A reduction also occurs when the athlete trains at one intensity or trains using the same exercises over a long training cycle. Accommodation can also take place during the competitive season when using the same program repetitively. To see improvement, one must almost adapt to training but never fully adapt.

While the Conjugate System was employed to advance the training efforts of high-skilled athletes, the Westside Conjugate System was also introduced to its 12- and 14-year-old athletes with phenomenal results. But the system is most important to teach the highest degree of sports-specific technique. The technique must continuously be reinforced throughout the athlete's entire career.

There are many things to learn about the Conjugate System. Let's start with Special Strength.

SPECIAL STRENGTHS

To understand Special Strengths, we will look at the individual categories for Special Strength Methods.

Maximal Effort Method

Special strengths start with the Maximal Effort Method, which is lifting a maximal or limit load. This method is best for improving both intramuscular and intermuscular coordination. The muscles and the central nervous system (CNS) will adapt only to the burden placed on them.

Supra-Maximal Method

With the addition of strong rubber bands, the lifter can handle a weight at the top with a much larger load than their current contest maximum. This is called the Combination of Resistance Method.

A female with a contest squat of 730 pounds made a parallel box squat with 500 pounds of band tension and 365 pounds of bar weight. This represents 865 pounds at lockout, which can only be accomplished with both bands and bar weight. There is no time limit on completing the effort and would include maximal isometrics.

A true M-E refers to one repetition only. It could be an all-time record, or it may be based on a daily max effort. The second method was used by the Bulgarian system.

Heavy-Efforts Method

The weights with the Heavy-Efforts Method will be 90 percent and above for several sets. The total lifts are four minimum, seven optimal, and ten lifts maximal. The reps are one to two reps per set.

Repeated Effort Method

The Repeated-Effort Method works best with small, special, single-joint exercises. Examples are back extensions or triceps extensions. The last reps in a set are the most beneficial for strength endurance or building muscle mass.

Dynamic Effort Method

The Dynamic-Effort Method is used by throwing a medicine ball or some sub-maximal implement at the highest velocity possible. This builds explosive strength. You should be lifting weights in the 75 to 80 percent range for speed strength at 0.8 to 0.9 m/s.

More can be found in *The Science and Practice of Strength Training* by V. M. Zatsiorsky and W.J. Kraemer.

Velocity Training

Special Strength is measured in a set velocity. Explosive Strength is trained at high speed. Thirty to 40 percent is most recommended. Explosive Strength is defined as the ability to rapidly increase force (Tidow, 1990). The steeper the increase of strength in time, the greater the explosive strength.

Speed Strength

Speed Strength is trained at 75 percent to 85 percent. It should be 50 percent of all training for weight lifters. Weightlifters have to be fast with heavy weights causing one to generate force (F=ma). If the mass is constant, it is best to increase acceleration.

Slow Strength

Slow Strength is just what it says. It requires the athlete to lift near-limit loads, so go to 97 percent for most training. Also known as Circa-Max Method, maximal strength will improve the speed of movement with near-maximal loads. It does not negatively affect the speed of movements with light loads.

Read *Science of Sports Training* by Thomas Kurz

Motion velocity decreases as the external load increases. Maximal force (Fmm) is attained when velocity is small, and maximum velocity (Vmm) is reached when external resistance is close to zero. (See also P. 29 *in Science and Practice of Strength Training* by V.M. Zatsiorsky and W. J. Kraemer. Also, refer to Hill's Equation of Muscle Contraction, P. 145 *Supertraining* by Mel Siff, Ph.D.)

Reactive Strength

Reactive Strength is your ability to go from a maximal force, mainly from an eccentric stretch, to a concentric action in a plyometric or a fast-rebound action.

SUMMARY

Let's summarize.

Both the Chinese and Westside have two maximum-effort (M-E) workouts a week. The Westside gym is for powerlifters, so it has an M-E day for the squat or deadlift where the lifters do two M-E lifts. (Example: It could be a box deadlift and a very-low box squat.) This is on Monday.

On Wednesday, it is M-E day for pressing. Again, it calls for two M-E lifts. (Example: A close-grip incline and a rack lockout.)

On Friday, it is a Dynamic workout for Speed-Strength at 75-80-85 percent in a three-week wave.

When the volume on M-E day is relatively low, but the Speed-Strength day is very high volume with 25 box squats and 25 deadlifts, the Speed-Strength day for pressing is 72 hours later on Saturday. This workout could be 9x3 reps, 6x6 reps, or 10x10 reps, with the weight ranging from 75-80-85 percent plus. And on all days, there should be small special exercises.

NOTE: The Conjugate System calls for the total barbell volume and intensity to fluctuate from high volume on Speed-Strength day to low volume on M-E day. As shown above, 80 percent of the training is on small special exercises or jumping, bounding, and working on flexibility. There also must be four small workouts with weights or jumping and bounding. This practice will be looked at carefully later in the book.

TRACK WORK

When training a sprinter, the M-E work should be performing 60- to 100-meter sprints as well as 200- to 300- and 400-meter sprints.

Doing both a weight-room M-E and a sprinting M-E is far too much and will lead to injuries or at least over-training. There are far too many injuries to sprinters, middle- and long-distance runners' lower bodies. Over-training can cause massive fatigue, irregular heartbeats and, in severe cases, can cause the kidneys to shut down.

Remember, no M-E gym work, and save the sprinting for your weekly Max-Effort plan.

Endurance

To increase endurance, you must push speed and strength. It should be known that weight training, even in the beginning, will contribute more to the most significant gains in distance sports than aerobic training.

It should be understood that the VO2 maximum levels in the highest skilled athletes stabilize, but their times improve. (Note: This information should tell the coach to stop running miles to race 100 meters. A high VO2 max is no guarantee of tremendous success.)

The running muscles and their oxidative levels are much more critical for improving endurance than the runner's cardio-respiratory ability. (See *Supertraining,* P. 247-248, and 249).

How to Test Your General Endurance

There are standard tests for endurance. One such test is lifting a barbell for a maximum number of lifts at 40 percent of a one-rep max. To evaluate the entire body is to do all classical lifts, but just one per workout. This will test your relative strength endurance.

Squat	**Deadlift**	**Snatch**
Bench	**Clean**	**Box jump**

Too much running can cause a speed barrier where one learns to move at a certain speed but no faster. To overcome a speed barrier, the athlete must do other forms of training, then resume running.

Let's Look at Basic Physics Equations

Work: defined as the product of net force and the displacement through which that force is exerted or W=Fd.

Power: defined as work done divided by the time used to do the work or W/T.

What does this have to do with running?

The more powerful sprinter will cover pre-set meters faster. But, if one runs with the same body weight and relative strength, they will only run so fast. This is the speed barrier.

THE CONJUGATE SYSTEM FOR
RUNNING

Let's provide the athlete with a weight sled to pull with three different weights. Here are some examples.

1. 20-30-40 pounds. The athlete can sprint with one weight at any distance of 60 to 80 meters for time. Now you have three records to break instead of just your body weight.

2. A weight vest can also be used with at least three different weights and specially weighted shorts.

3. Also, run with a wheelbarrow with three weights for any distance.

The athlete now has 12 resistance tests to evaluate his or her speed rather than just bodyweight. The different resistances must be rotated to avoid the Law of Accommodation. Keep a training log to check times and progress with each weight.

Special exercises have no eight, ten, or 12-week cycles. An athlete must switch when their body or mind does not respond to the exercises. The more extroverted the athlete, the more special exercises they need as well as changing the exercises more often. An introverted athlete can switch less often. Coach, know your athlete's mental state!

Type 1 Slow-Twitch, or Slow Oxidative

Slow-Twitch runners are more resistant to fatigue in long-distance running, cycling, and other similar sports activities. Their muscle fibers respond to weights up to 70 percent.

Type IIA Fast-Twitch Oxidative

Fast-Twitch runners work with both aerobic and anaerobic challenges and are suitable for all sports. They work well with 75 to 80 percent workouts.

Type IIB Fast-Twitch Glycolytic

Type IIB fiber type produces maximal force when exercising. This type of athlete works best with sprinting, Olympic weightlifting, or powerlifting. They respond best with 90 to 100 percent exertion.

USING THE CONJUGATE SYSTEM FOR
TIME

The famous coach Glen Mill set times to cover a distance. Westside has used this time system to increase the length of acceleration and some top speed maintenance using three, seven, ten, and 15-second periods.

At the set time limit, you check the distance covered. For example, Usain Bolt covered 110 meters in 10.6 seconds. For much longer distances, the same method can be used, but the times are much longer.

Speed Endurance

To main top speed for a prolonged time requires interval training. You use a set amount of work with a set rest interval between working sets.

Speed endurance is the ability to maintain top speed for as long as possible. To test your speed endurance, start by running for 15 seconds and mark the distance covered. Rest fully and repeat, trying to extend the distance. Three or four sets are optimal before fatigue sets in. Each time you extend the distance, you have increased your top speed maintenance.

For longer races, such as 800, 100, or 1500 meters, you must use a more extended time limit: 800-meter run for 60 seconds; 1500 meters run for 120 seconds.

Each time mark your distance covered, fully rest, and try to cover a longer distance.

For one mile, 3000, and 5000 meters, lengthen the distance, remember to mark the place, and then rest and repeat. All the while, try to add length on each run. This will help your top-speed maintenance. By constantly exceeding the last distance covered, you have added to your speed endurance.

Use just bodyweight, weight, vest with three different weights, weight sled with three different weights, and run with a wheelbarrow with different weights. Rotate the resistance when no progress can be made due to lack of enthusiasm or physical fatigue. The athlete must be motivated at all times. Three-week waves are very effective.

Suppose one uses a weight training workout for strength. In that case, it should be done before a long endurance workout to create the feeling that bodyweight training is easy compared to heavy efforts. Use a set time between strength and endurance workouts.

Only train one task at a time. There is always a side effect to any physical training, which is fatigue. This is known as the two-factor theory of fitness fatigue. Fitness or strength is not stable but is up and down.

Physical fitness shows the athlete's preparedness throughout the year. It is easy to lower fitness due to stress, overtraining, or one's mental state at meet time. It can take ten months, however, to build an athlete's top level of preparedness. You can gain fitness or strength during workouts, but it is accompanied by some fatigue. Fatigue is then followed by a rest recovery period, then the process is repeated. It is true to say the fitness or strength you gain is longer lasting than the time to recover from fatigue.

Large volume workouts can be done every 72 hours. Small workouts 30 minutes or less can be done in 12 to 24 hours. These periods have been proven through studies by many other experts and Westside Barbell's training. For example, the Chinese perform two M-E workouts a week using Olympic lifting exercises. Westside uses powerlifting exercises with the same positive results.

Remember, more swimming or skating is not the answer to better swimming or skating. Instead, weight training with six to eight exercise circuits will bring more success.

LOCALIZED ENDURANCE

Many times, a single muscle or muscle group will suffer from acute fatigue. This is due to accentuation. Accentuation occurs in the main range of the sports movement, where the demand for high-force production is maximal. (Note: More on accentuation in *Science and Practice of Strength Training*, P. 122.)

For most accentuation training, extensions are used: triceps extensions, back extensions, leg lifts, thigh extensions, isometrics in the correct angles, and Reverse Hypers TM. Always consider the relationship between force and posture.

Yes, Isometrics will build muscular endurance in positions in postures that your sport requires. Muscular endurance is developed in heavy weight training, where activation of the cardiovascular or respiratory systems is used.

All workouts must not only be rotated when necessary, but weights, distance, and times must be logged. One device that can handle this chore for you is the GPS Performance Tracker Vest.

NOTE:
When doing Isometrics, accommodation happens very fast. It is recommended to do four to six times a week if you intend to increase Fmm .08 and twice a week for maintaining your strength gain.

LET'S LOOK BACK

General endurance is the ability to perform for a long time involving most muscle groups. Directed endurance is similar to general endurance but is aimed at changing to sport-specific training such as jumping. Sport-specific endurance is overcoming fatigue in legs for running and jumping or maintaining fast hands while in combat sports. More can be found in *Explosive Power and Jumping Ability* by T. Starzynski and H. Sozanski.

All three types of endurance can be overlapped in training. The Conjugate System allows all manners of training when needed. Never inside a Block System! The Block System has no leeway for overlapping activities.

The Conjugate System allows the coach or athlete to boost a missing element of training in a weekly plan. The weekly training plan can include circuit training, ballgames, an obstacle course, or other inventive ways to increase endurance.

"Not being willing to TRY is the beginning of the end"

Accommodating Resistance

Like all training, the Conjugate System must be utilized in special strength training to produce the results you want. In this chapter, we'll focus on special strengths, the relationship between force and velocity, and what that has to do with Accommodating Resistance (AR) Methods. But this chapter is not only about AR. It is also about distinguishing Special Strengths concerning sub-maximal weight training that requires the weight to move at a certain speed. For this, you must use Combinations of Resistance Training.

SPECIAL STRENGTHS

The first thing you need to understand is that Special Strengths—Explosive Strength, Speed-Strength, Strength-Speed, and Isometrics--are measured by velocity.

- Explosive Strength is developed in fast velocity at 30 percent to 40 percent of a one-rep max.
- Speed-Strength is developed in intermediate velocity at 75 percent to 85 percent of a one-rep max.
- Strength-Speed is developed in slow velocity at 90 percent and above.
- Isometrics are developed at zero velocity.

The coach must know Special Strengths and their individual velocities to understand the differences in these velocities. It is fully explained by the relationship between force and velocity.

Motion velocity decreases as external resistance increases. This means that maximum force (Fmm) is developed when velocity is small. When maximum velocity (Vmm) is attained, external resistance is close to zero.

The Conjugate System can utilize all four special strengths at the same time. The Westside System runs Explosive-Strength and Speed-Strength in three-week waves.

Explosive Strength

Each Friday, Westside runs week one at 30 percent, week two at 35 percent, and week three at 40 percent to develop Explosive Strength. Using the five classic lifts—squat, bench, deadlift, snatch and clean, and clean and jerk—plus the Goodmorning, the optimal number of lifts is 30, the maximum is 36 lifts, and the minimum is 24 lifts.

Speed-Strength

Speed-Strength is trained at 75 percent to 85 percent in a three-week wave, week one at 75 percent, week two at 80 percent, and week three at 85 percent. Using A.S. Prilepin's (1974) data, at 70 percent, the number of lifts is 12 minimum, 18 optimal, and 24 lifts maximum.

Max-Effort Workouts

Westside has two M-E days a week. One for the upper body and one for the lower body. On M-E days, Westside works up to a new max on some special exercise with a record-breaking lift at about 90 to 95 percent of all-time. Athletes will work up to a new all-time max by 90-, 95-, 100 percent-plus on two lifts.

This is three lifts above 90 percent up to a new all-time personal record on both upper and lower body days to bring the total to six lifts above 90 percent a week.

During week three on Speed-Strength day, the advanced Westside men and women lift other 90 percent weights by using Compensatory Acceleration Training, also known as CAT.

UNDERSTANDING
COMPENSATORY ACCELERATION TRAINING

In the late 1970s, Dr. Squat, aka Fred Hatfield, said no one could lift a heavy weight slowly. He explained that you had to accelerate throughout the entire range of motion.

Dr. Squat provided an example of CAT, but there is a significant problem when lifting a submaximal load because of the relationship between force and posture. As the weight bar nears completion, the force on the bar is diminished as velocity slows to zero. This is illustrated on P. 40 in Science and Practice of Strength Training. The authors also explained the force-velocity curve on Page 29.

If only barbell weight is used, you have a problem. There cannot be a perfect weight at the top and the bottom. A weight that the athlete can barely lift out of the rack will undoubtedly cause them to miss in the bottom. If a weight is light in the bottom, then it will be light at the completion of the lift producing little force at the top due to the relationship between force and velocity. (Once again, see P. 29 in Science and Practice of Strength Training.)

WHAT IS THE ANSWER?
The Combination of Resistance Methods

What is Accommodating Resistance (AR)? It is the method of training to develop maximal tension throughout the entire range of motion. This is nothing new, as you might think. The first machine was made by Zander in 1879, primarily for medical use. Then, Nautilus used a variable lever arm to provide Accommodating Resistance. One problem, however, is that a machine will build muscle, but not motion, meaning coordination. A better method is to use bands or chains or both.

Using bands, chains, or both is the correct method for Accommodating Resistance. Dr. Mel Siff spent quite a bit of time at Westside watching me use first chains and later rubber bands with a barbell. Dr. Siff actually coined the phrase "Combination of Resistance Methods" for my work designing the tools for Westside Barbell lifters to break world records.

Muscular force changes as joint angles change. CAT was the correct method to produce force throughout the entire range of motion of any barbell movement. But it had limitations due to favorable joint angles or changes in the force-velocity curve. Most weight that could be moved strongly at the start—meaning the bottom—would be moving too fast at the top for the muscles' or joints' strength curves. To answer this problem, we attached chains or bands to the bar.

The first experiments were with chains that would deload on the eccentric phase and then reload on the concentric phase. For 18 months, Westside experimented with different chain percents compared to barbell weight.

The experiments established that 25 percent of the total load be made up of chains for intermediate velocity training. For Speed-Strength, that is 75 percent to 85 percent. Following these results means a 600-pound max squat would use 150 pounds of chain during a three-week wave. An 800-pound max squat would raise the chain resistance to 200 pounds of chain. And a 1,000-pound max squat would use 250 pounds to make the lift's bottom fast enough to maintain close to 0.8 m/s.

For Strength-Speed, 50 percent of the load would be chain weight. Significant progress was made, including world records. Twenty-five percent of the total load for Explosive Strength was also 25 percent of the total band tension for Explosive Strength or 30 percent to 40 percent of total weight.

Chains have some negative aspects. It is challenging to set the chains the exact way each time you bench or deadlift. Nor do just chains provide any over-speed eccentrics. The chains must be connected to the bar by a small ¼ inch chain to set the chain's height to unload at the bottom of the lift. Four-foot-long, 5/8" chain works best for unloading, which is hooked through the ¼" chain and hung like a horseshoe. By using a chain, you have two different strength curves.

BAND TRAINING

After using chains to AR, Coach Dave Williams of Liberty University asked if the author would experiment with strong rubber bands. The rubber bands had been used only for stretching, but the coach said he wanted to attach them to a barbell.

At first, the bands had to be weighted at the top of the lift, but they also had to have strong tension at the bottom to provide constant pressure throughout the full range of motion.

The next question was how much tension each band could provide. For benching, the bands were attached under a 4x4 block of wood one inch off the floor. All bench bands were doubled up. A mini set provided 85 pounds of tension. A monster set provided 125 pounds of tension. A light band set provided 200 pounds of tension.

When training at an average total weight or resistance of 80 percent with roughly 33 percent band tension with a mini or monster band, a 400-pound max bench would have a mini-band tension of 85 pounds and 235 pounds bar weight. This brings the total combination to 320 pounds or 80 percent of a 400-pound max bench.

Using bands will change the posture and the strength curves. The strength that an athlete can produce in any motion will depend on the body's posture or joint angle. This shows that the maximal force one can produce on a barbell relies on the height of the bar.

Using bands will alter the normal strength curve that just barbell weight alone delivers using AR with chain or bands. With AR on the barbell, it can also change the sticking point. Bands can add over-speed eccentrics or power metrics to the bar while also adding to reversible muscle action. Chains do not; they only act as AR.

When squatting for Speed-Strength, 25 percent to 33 percent band tension works well. If the goal is to build maximal or Slow-Strength when the velocity is close to zero, more band tension must be used to slow the barbell to completion. For example, two 760-pound squats placed 500 pounds of band tension and maxed at 385 pounds of bar weight. This represented 885 pounds at lockout.

For circa max training, 375 pounds of band tension and 600 pounds of bar weight, which equals 975 pounds, will produce a contest squat of 900 pounds. This is a single off of a parallel box squat. Four hundred forty pounds of band tension and 600 pounds bar weight is required for a circa max cycle for a 1,000-pound squat. That is 44 percent band tension. It adds up to 1,040 pounds on a max squat. As you can see, it is 44 percent of a 1,000-pound squat.

Circa Max weights are 90 percent to 97 percent of a one-rep max while slowly stretching the bands.

You can use different amounts of bands with tensions ranging from 85 pounds to 720 pounds at lockout to change the velocities during several workouts while Accommodating Resistance for Explosive Strength, Speed-Strength, Slow-Strength, and Circa-Max Strength.

Bands also can be used for functional Isometrics or the Hoffman Method of Isometrics. You can attach a set of strong enough bands to lift against where the bar will only be raised to a certain height in those cases. At that point, the combination of bar weight and band tension becomes too strong to move higher. At that point, hold at that position, Isometrically for a set time limit.

By constantly making changes in velocities, the body will not accommodate and will continue to adapt to different stimuli. This is the Conjugate System—continually going from one intensity, one speed but constantly rotating without breaking the training stimulus for furthering the training protocol.

If an athlete only achieves a max in a classical lift, squat, bench, deadlift, snatch, or the clean and jerk, they would only have one indicator toward their progress. But there is a more sophisticated method to measure your progress.

Here is an example. Our 123-pound to 132-pound male lifter Jeremy Smith holds the raw 123-pound world record at 556 pounds and 670 pounds in gear meet. At 132 pounds, his best squat is 760 pounds. Before making the 760-pound world record, he made a Combination of Methods record on a box with 440 pounds of bands plus 475 pounds bar weight, which equals 915 pounds. He also made a record on a box with 500 pounds of bands and 505-pound bar weight. This equals 1,005 pounds. His best box squat with just bar weight is 685 pounds in briefs.

NOTE:

a 10 percent to 15 percent higher squat is standard for most, which would be very close to his world record of 760 pounds.

The key to Westside's Conjugate training success is Jeremy has at least special box squat records that when he breaks one, his regular contest squat also will be at a standard. This is much less stressful on your mental state if you miss, which with proper training, Westside does not miss.

Adding chains and bands to the arsenal of training methods and training at every velocity will eliminate the Law of Accommodation by changing special barbell exercises each week and running three-week waves for Explosive Strength or Speed-Strength. This is the Conjugate System.

"Big Aint Strong,
Strong is Strong."
—Louie Simmons

CHAPTER 3
CONJUGATE JUMPING

I t is imperative to include jumping in an athlete's preparation for sports of all kinds. In most sports, jumping ability is the most crucial ability in raising fitness. An athlete must jump in all sports, especially in gymnastics, skiing, and, of course, track and field, to develop explosive power.

WHAT IS **EXPLOSIVE POWER?**

Explosive power is the ability to rapidly increase force (Tidow, 1990). The faster increase in strength in time, the greater the explosive strength.

Developing and Measuring Jumping Ability

To develop good elasticity of the muscles used for takeoffs and neuromuscular coordination to increase jumping ability, the athlete must do many repetitions and movements that resemble jumping. Jumping endurance can be raised by many repetitions in slightly different forms of special jumping and reactive methods.

To test jumping ability, jump onto a box or perform a reach jump.

SPECIAL JUMPING

General Jumping

General jumps are not aimed at only one sport but rather at the development of the entire body. At the same time, however, they are geared toward later specialization for a sport or event.

Directed Jumping

Directed jumps must be close in timing and structure to an event, such as high jumps and long jumps. The athlete must raise the level of strength in the legs and torso and increase ability and flexibility.

Sport-Specific Jumps

Sport-specific jumps refer to track and field events and basketball dunks, jumping to catch a football or baseball, spiking a volleyball, and the like.

The Conjugate System allows for all three jumping categories to be used during the same time frame, if necessary, to further the athlete's jumping ability. Jumping rope, performing depth jumps, and other training means, such as sprinting or pulling a weight sled, are used. Many special exercises will strengthen all the athlete's muscles.

All muscles do not develop at the same rate, however. If one muscle group lags behind, progress will slow or stop. Or worse, a possible injury can occur. Thankfully, all the special barbell squats and pulls and the countless small single-joint exercises will increase endurance, Speed-Strength and the ability to direct one's body movements.

For jumping, not only does one have to raise explosive strength, but also maximal strength. Strength is the ability to overcome external resistance or to resist it through muscular efforts. As defined in Newton's second law of dynamics, explosive strength is a product of mass and its acceleration.

We have talked about the three types of jumping. It must be understood that the Conjugate System of Jumping does not call for special blocks of one kind of jump. Instead, it introduces general jumping—like even box jumps—during the competitive season, where sport-specific exercises are used most.

No one is a fortune teller and can undoubtedly know the actual progress the athlete will make by contest time.

Sports fitness is built over many years where there is a constant gain in speed, strength, and coordination. These elements must be raised concurrently. If one falls short, they all fall short. Each ability brings improvements to the other special abilities to increase jumping.

Remember the first time you box jumped on a 36-inch box, or you could deadlift 330 pounds, or even the first time you tried to deadlift? Did you ever stop and ask yourself how you did it with zero practice? The childhood games and other activities had little to do with the box jump or deadlift. Still, those activities and the Conjugate System of undirected work contributed to your first success. Another name for it, of course, is GPP. Now that you are not a child but rather a young (or old) athlete, you need to enter a well-planned and sophisticated training regiment directed to a sport or an event.

PREPARE TO JUMP

Without a plan, you plan to fail. Let's look at a selection of special jumping exercises.

Kneeling Jumps

Start by sitting on your knees. Rock back to place your glutes on your heels, then jump onto your feet. After you can do this, place a barbell on your back and jump onto your feet from the same starting position.

Move on to doing a power clean off your knees. When you master this, perform a snatch off your knees. First with a square stance, then onto a split-style snatch.

For the youngest jumpers, perform a seated press off the floor. Start with the bar across your legs and clean and press. Next, while sitting on the floor, perform a snatch.

Only do one or two types of kneeling jumps in one workout. Then, rotate to the second set of kneeling jumps after three jump sessions.

The kneeling jumps are meant for preparing one to jump. They can be introduced into various training, from general exercises to directed exercises to sport-specific activities. Remember, don't become locked into block-style training. Even while doing sport-specific training, some may have to return to a much more basic approach.

The number of special jumps can go from 24 jumps two times a week to 40 jumps two times a week to 40 jumps three times a week. On the fourth week, return to 24 two times a week for restoration. Then, move on to week two and week three.

Do not train in blocks, but do what is necessary at the time—no matter what time of the training year.

GENERAL JUMPING

General jumping, like general exercises, is non-specific to any sport but will enhance the body for specialization later on. This could be any ball sport, winter sports, and, of course, all track and field. General exercise should also include single-joint activities used to bring up a weak muscle or muscle group.

For general jumping, use even boxes, jump up then down, and with a fast absorption phase, jump up onto a second box and repeat. This style of jumping will increase explosive strength and improve the weaker muscles used for jumping.

General jumping, along with general exercises, can be used during directed jumping, meaning jumps close to the pattern of contest jumps. They can also be used while training an athlete's competitive sport.

The key to training is to never break the connection from workout to workout. If one simply restricts an athlete's activity to one type, accommodation will raise its ugly head. It should be clear the many kinds of jumping must be trained inside a weekly, monthly, and multi-year plan.

To build eccentric strength for a faster rate of amortizing strength, jump down from a higher box and rebound to a shorter box. For concentric actions, drop off a lower box and rebound to a much higher box. It is essential to increase all three jump training types.

All jumps should be measured by doing a jump test. In a jump test, rebound up to touch a hanging object or touch the wall and place a marker at the top height.

When doing concentric power, the box you use for depth jumps should not exceed 20 inches for most athletes. If you raise the box you drop from, and your jump height goes down, the box is too high, and your amortization phase becomes too long. This means your elastic energy is reduced.

Do not ever let this happen.

When depth jumps are performed off boxes 36 inches and up, you will build maximal strength but have a longer amortization or absorption phase.

For beginners, do two sets of 24 jumps two times a week. For the well-conditioned and mature athletes, do 40 jumps two times a week. Highly skilled athletes can do 40 jumps three times per week for optimal training.

Box jumping can be done with ankle weight, weight vest, and Kettlebells. Keep meticulous records noting all resistances, and rotate from one to another type of resistances. You must also change the number of jumps per set.

Training must be just that—training, not work. So, rotate to keep training fun but connected. This is a rule for all jumps. You may want to consider the following to mix things up:

- Bounding on one foot or two feet
- Ten jumps using both legs with two heights of 36 inches and 42 inches for well-trained
- Six to 12 jumps on one leg
- Six to 12 jumps on one leg, switching legs
- Six to 12 jumps alternating from right leg to left leg
- Adding a lightweight vest, or Kettlebells
- Include even and uneven height boxes
- Walking up and down steps with barbell or Kettlebells
- Ukrainian deadlifts or jumps while standing on two Ply-O boxes
- Jumps with barbell on back
- Sep-ups with and without weights
- One-legged squats

MINI-JUMPS OR BOUNDING

Doing a series of jumps will help quickness. Quickness is the ability to fire the central nervous system to contract, relax, or control muscle function without the involvement of any preliminary stretch, which can increase reaction time. By training with 30 percent to 40 percent weights, Explosive Strength can be significantly improved.

The shock method using plyometric exercises, like Death Jumps, will improve your reaction time as well. Also, contract methods are used for better reaction times. You would lift a 90 percent barbell for one to two reps, then immediately lift a load of 30 percent to 40 percent for three to five reps. You can also lift a 90-percent barbell for one to two reps and then jump up on a box.

Or, you can use weight releasers. Load a barbell to 60 percent of a one-rep max, then place a set of weight releasers with an additional 20 percent that equals a total of 80 percent on the eccentric phase. Release the 20 percent on the weight releasers and perform the concentric phase as fast as possible.

Westside has found that the Static Dynamic Method is superior to all others. Westside has both US and EU patents on its Static-Dynamic Developer. It allows you to load weight from 30 percent to 40 percent, then set the brake on the device and have the athlete pull or push gradually up to 100 percent effort for two or three seconds. Then, you release the brake and move the load as fast as possible.

By rotating the exercises above, you will train at 100 percent all the time by simply interchanging special exercises when the athlete feels staleness in the muscles or mind.

Everything works, but nothing works forever. This is a simple explanation of the Conjugate System.

When doing depth jumps at about 20 inches, they will produce a higher force in pulse on the active push phase than squats with 30 percent to 60 percent or jumping without weight. For top athletes, 75 cm will yield the highest rebound. Going up to 95 cm and even 155 cm caused the rebound or force impulse to be lower due to a slower and longer amortization phase.

But the higher depth jumps increase maximal strength due to the total muscular working force developed by eccentric amortization followed by active concentric action. This causes elastic energy equal to the K-E of the athlete at the end of the fall.

As you can see, there are several jumps and jump methods to rotate in and out of for a three-week cycle. If the training effect is diminished, switch to a jump proven to work for the individual athlete. There are different weight training exercises and single-joint movements to enhance their performance. High volume and low volume jumping must be interchanged during a three-week wave.

Even restoration methods also will be rotated. Large workouts must be separated by 72 hours, and small workouts must be separated by 24 or 12 hours.

A sprinter should do their M-E workouts on the track leaving the Explosive Strength and Speed-Strength exercises in the gym to avoid overtraining and injuries.

Do not write a program and think it will work for any length of time without modification. You'll need the flexibility to add some special exercises for a single-joint issue, meaning hamstrings, glutes, calves, or any muscle group that is lagging. Or the problem could be working on your timing. It could be that you need more strength or more explosive power. No one can know what is ahead and what is behind after six to eight weeks into the program.

You should know what you need and add it to the training while eliminating what is not working. This is the Conjugate System.

"Don't be afraid to fail or look like a fool. These are necessary milestones towards greatness"

—Louie Simmons

CONJUGATE FOR PERIODIZATION

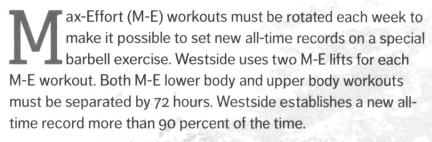

Max-Effort (M-E) workouts must be rotated each week to make it possible to set new all-time records on a special barbell exercise. Westside uses two M-E lifts for each M-E workout. Both M-E lower body and upper body workouts must be separated by 72 hours. Westside establishes a new all-time record more than 90 percent of the time.

M-E work by total volume is much less than on Speed-Strength day. On M-E day, a weight of 90 percent, 95 percent, or 100-plus is done twice in a workout. This is six lifts for single on M-E day — high intensity but low volume with the barbell.

Compare this to Speed-Strength with 75, 80, or 80 percent weights for Olympic weightlifters. For powerlifters, it is 80, 85, or 90 percent. They lift in three-week waves for 5x5 reps on the box squat and 5x5 reps on some style of deadlifting for 50 total lifts.

The M-E training and Explosive or Speed-Strength training are vastly different in both intensity and total volume.

Bands and chains must be added to the equation. The key to periodization is that it presents a plan to follow in a weekly program for M-E workouts and three-week waves where a percent of a one-rep max goes up by five percent each week for three weeks. After three weeks, the weight drops 10 percent, and the three-week process is repeated.

Many times, the bar will be interchanged with a bar for the squat and bench. You can use a safety-squat bar, bow bar, 14-inch camber bar, bulldog-squat bar, or a front-squat bar.

The three-week waves will be used throughout the monthly, yearly, and multi-year plans. Seventy-two hours later, an M-E workout will be rotated each week with a pull one week and a squat the next. Goodmornings can also be added. The cycles will have three-week waves, circa-max workouts, super-maximal days where the band tension far exceeds the barbell weight, strength cycles, and much more.

DIVISION INTO
TRAINING PERIODS

I knew Western periodization was a dead-end as early as 1973, which was the year I broke my back for the first time, but I knew no other way. In 1983 after breaking my L5 the second time, I had to find a better way. I would be strong in one lift, but not the other two. It would be a different lift that would go up while some other lifts were unmanageable. Ricky Crain, a great lifter, would call me with the same story. Dave Waddington, the first 1,000-pound squatter, was in my living room and asked how to fix the same problem that Ricky and I had. I would tell him when he found the answer to call me.

So back to 1981. I was desperate. I made a call to Bud Charniga to buy some Soviet books on training. He said, "Lou, you know these are like textbooks written by their Sports scientists on very intricate matters on training." I told Bud that textbooks were precisely what I needed because the Western gradual overload system led me down a dead-end road. It is more of a detraining system than anything else. Enough talking about the past.

I looked at the models of Matveyev, his wave system, and the wave-like concentration of loading for five to eight weeks at a time by Verkhoshansky. I then looked at a pendulum approach by Arosiev, which is used for alternating special strength preparation such as Speed-Strength, Explosive Strength, Strength-Speed, and even Strength Endurance. I also looked at Tudor O. Bompa, Ph.D., and his findings. It was interesting how effective the system was that made Naim Suleymanoglu the great Bulgarian weight lifter. I realized the design was for a model athlete or someone of perfect proportion for his sport. It was based on the hypothesis of Felix Meerson from *Plasticeskoe Obezpecenie Organizma* (1967) and Hiden's findings from1960-1964.

Which one was the best, or was there a best? These were, after all, knowledgeable men, to say the least, but I found before that I did not like a long-term plan. In my training and my training plateaus, I discovered that I would regress almost every time after going upward for three weeks. I liked the wave system of training by Matveyev and Verkhoshansky, but Vorobyev's (1978) wave plan was somewhat less restrictive, somewhat like Ermakov's work in 1974.

Dr. Siff asked me how I came up with a three-week Speed-Strength wave. I told him I became no stronger or faster after three weeks, and he was fascinated to hear that because V. Alexez, the great Soviet SHW lifter, used the same three-week wave. On week four, he reevaluated the training and started a new three-week wave cycle. I think I won Mel Siff over at that time.

I implement different approaches. I seldom do a regular squat or deadlift. The bench is done, but with very light percents, roughly 40 percent to 50 percent, with the addition of accommodating resistance. As the meet approaches, we don't reduce special exercises but push them to the limit to perfect form by concentrating on the weak muscle group. This is what the conjugate system does. We use three strength training phases, including Maximal Effort, the Dynamic Method, and the Repetition Method for hypertrophy, all trained simultaneously. The three-week pendulum wave has built-in flexibility.

The first graphs concerning volume and intensities zones also show the importance of waving the volume and percentage of a one-rep max again to avoid accommodation. The speed-strength days show high volume and moderate to low intensity. On max effort days, the opposite will and must occur. The volume is 35 percent to 50 percent of the speed days, but as the intensities must be as high as possible, a new all-time record will hopefully be set. Like the Bulgarian, preparedness is the primary factor for how much one can lift on Max-Effort day.

The following graphs show volume and intensities:

FIGURE 1.1
SQUAT AND DEADLIFT MAX EFFORT DAY

■ **Intesity Zone**   ■ Total Volume

Low Volume training; highest intensity possible for 100 percent and above. Limit to three lifts of 90 percent and above to all-time max.

FIGURE 1.2
SQUAT AND SPEED STRENGTH

High volume training; Moderate intensity zones between 60 percent to 85 percent. Limit to 12 to 24 lifts per training session.

FIGURE 1.3
BENCH SPEED DAY

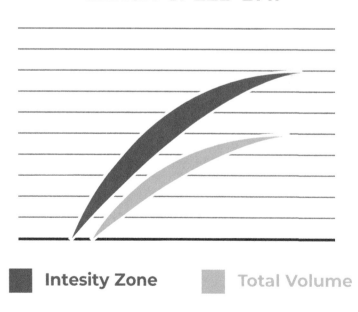

High Volume training; Low to moderate intensity between 50 percent to 60 percent. Limit 16 to 30 lifts per training session.

FIGURE 1.4
BENCH MAX EFFORT

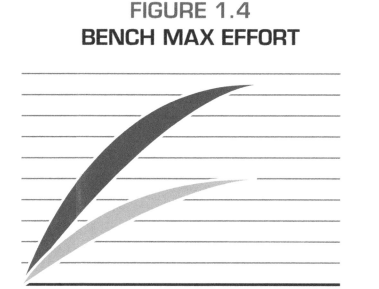

■ Intesity Zone   ■ Total Volume

Low volume training; highest intensity possible. Limit to three lifts of 90 percent and above to all-time max.

There are four direct periods of periodization

1. **Accumulation** — high volume of training of all types to charge or build the body for speed or strength for a particular sport.

2. **Intensification** — the athlete now limits the exercises focusing on more specific speed work or strength movements that work best for him.

3. **Transformation** — now, the values of the previous two cycles are tested while the athlete uses exercises that are most beneficial to the competition. The top lifters use a circa-max or near-max weight phase with limited special exercises contributing to their highest achievements for lifting. A runner's work would be very limited to the very most important speed or speed endurance work.

4. **Delayed Transformation** — the athlete reduces the high-intensity work and relies on rest and restoration for two to four weeks leading to a competition.

It is imperative to know about these phases of training. Refer to the suggested reading for more information on periodization.

During the Westside system of using a three-week wave for Speed-Strength and Explosive-Speed training, the wave rotates from 75 percent to 85 percent in a three-week cycle, jumping five percent per week. By doing this, I can evaluate the progress of the athlete all the time. This makes more sense to observe if the athlete has become stronger or faster and other physical qualities such as quickness or muscle mass. I don't have a crystal ball, so I have no idea how the athlete will progress in 12 weeks or 24 weeks. The three-week wave system allows for better observation continuously for maximal effort work each week. The major barbell exercises are changed.

Soviet sports scientists found after three weeks of weight training at 90 percent or more, progress stopped. This is accommodation, but it is totally eliminated by revolving the barbell exercises each week. We can max out every week throughout the year, and extreme workouts can occur every 72 hours. Our weekly plan is to speed squat on Friday with a high volume of 75 percent to 85 percent intensity zone for three reps per set. On Monday, it is Max-Effort work for squatting or pulling for max singles. The intensity is 100 percent plus all an individual can do on that particular day, similar to the Bulgarian system. No more than three lifts from 90 percent up to a new max; of course, the volume is low, much like the Rule of 60 Percent. Speed bench on Sunday. High volume and very-low intensity zones range from 40 percent to 50 percent. Wednesday is Max-Effort day, working up to a new personal record or as much as possible with single lifts not more than three lifts at 90 percent, approaching 100 percent; plus, in one week, the speed work is 20 to 30 lifts while the max effort day is three lifts. It is almost a 10 to one ratio, with speed lifts beginning the ten and max lifts being one.

The bulk of our system is special exercises. We do not have a system to form a model athlete, so it may take several combinations of special exercises to help one succeed. Our entire training program is built around special exercises for weightlifting, powerlifting or running, and jumping. I don't concentrate on what you have, but rather what you don't have.

An NFL agent brought in a lineman and asked me what I was going to do. I told him, and he said, "Why aren't you going to run him?" I asked him this question, "He ran for four years, and this is how fast he is. Why do you think two more months of running with him will make a difference?" He replied, "Good point."

Let's look at pendulum waves with special bars. The graphs show a nine-week training cycle consisting of three different three-week pendulum waves. The nine-week system employs three types of bars. They each have a maximum weight to calculate the percentages. All three maximums are different to avoid the mistake of accommodation or using the same volume repeatedly. The bar path will be somewhat different as well to ensure training all the leg and back muscles. The bar speed by percentage will be close, but the bar weight is quite different.

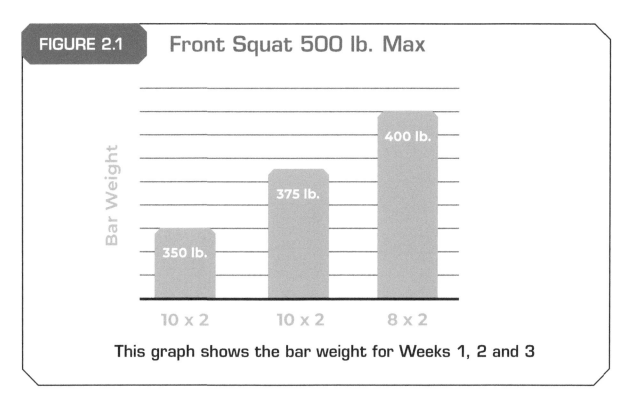

FIGURE 2.1 Front Squat 500 lb. Max

Bar Weight

350 lb.
375 lb.
400 lb.

10 x 2   10 x 2   8 x 2

This graph shows the bar weight for Weeks 1, 2 and 3

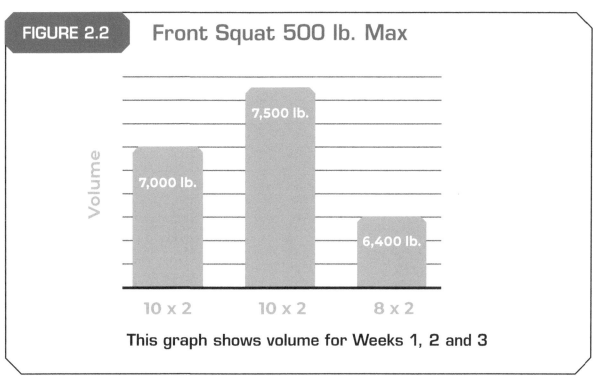

FIGURE 2.2 Front Squat 500 lb. Max

Volume

7,500 lb.
7,000 lb.
6,400 lb.

10 x 2   10 x 2   8 x 2

This graph shows volume for Weeks 1, 2 and 3

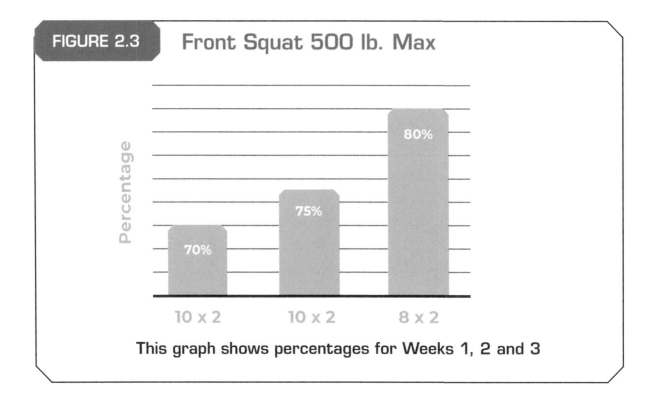

FIGURE 2.3

Front Squat 500 lb. Max

Percentage

| 70% | 75% | 80% |

| 10 x 2 | 10 x 2 | 8 x 2 |

This graph shows percentages for Weeks 1, 2 and 3

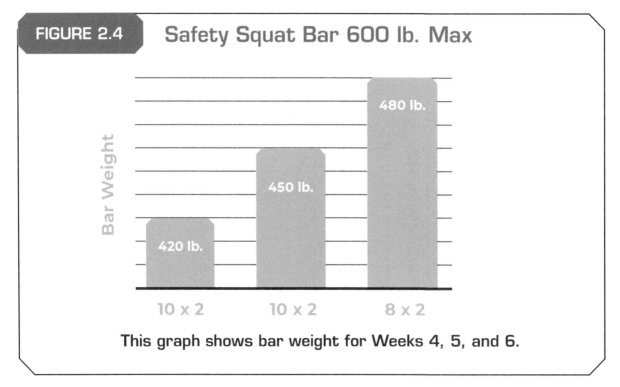

FIGURE 2.4

Safety Squat Bar 600 lb. Max

Bar Weight

| 420 lb. | 450 lb. | 480 lb. |

| 10 x 2 | 10 x 2 | 8 x 2 |

This graph shows bar weight for Weeks 4, 5, and 6.

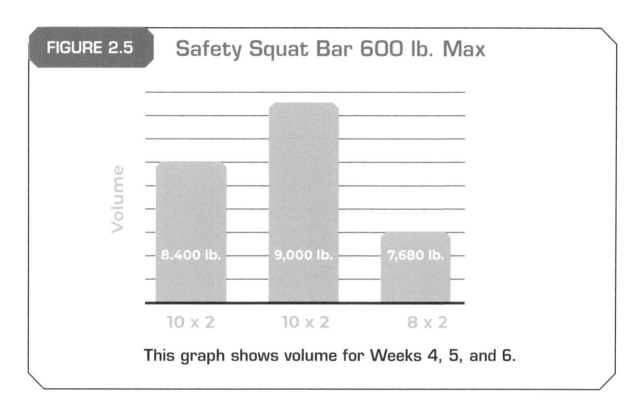

This graph shows volume for Weeks 4, 5, and 6.

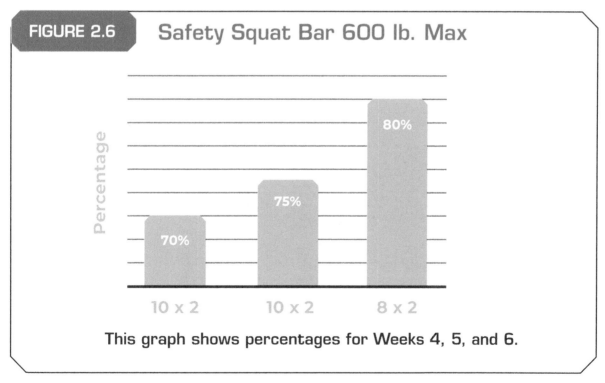

This graph shows percentages for Weeks 4, 5, and 6.

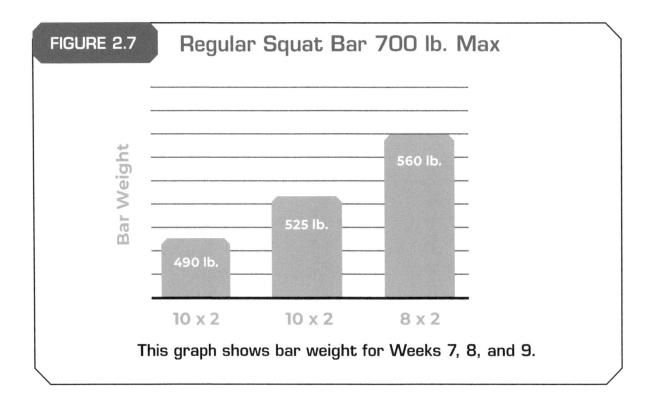

FIGURE 2.7

Regular Squat Bar 700 lb. Max

Bar Weight

490 lb. — 10 x 2
525 lb. — 10 x 2
560 lb. — 8 x 2

This graph shows bar weight for Weeks 7, 8, and 9.

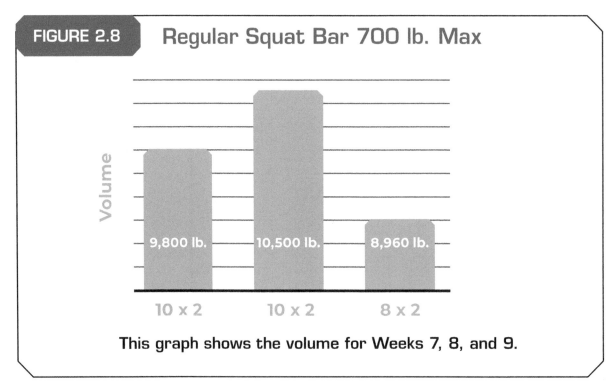

FIGURE 2.8

Regular Squat Bar 700 lb. Max

Volume

9,800 lb. — 10 x 2
10,500 lb. — 10 x 2
8,960 lb. — 8 x 2

This graph shows the volume for Weeks 7, 8, and 9.

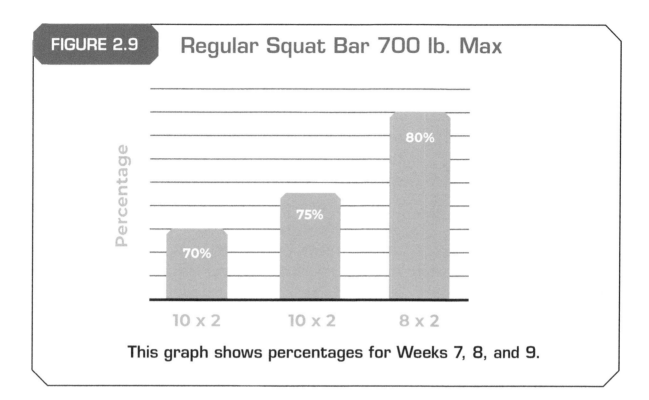

FIGURE 2.9 Regular Squat Bar 700 lb. Max

Percentage

80%

75%

70%

10 x 2   10 x 2   8 x 2

This graph shows percentages for Weeks 7, 8, and 9.

The wave cycles vary as bands, chains, or combinations are added to the barbell to accommodate resistance. When using weight releasers, the added weight on the first eccentric rep phase can be calculated. The variations of a wave are too numerous to list.

Typically, the Speed-Strength waves for squatting and benching continue for three weeks, and the strength speed waves last only two weeks due to their severity and the near-max or circa-max wave phases. If the Speed Day waves are of ultra-high volume for squatting with speed pulls following, the squats are also of high-volume workout. A Speed-Strength squat day is followed by a maximal effort day 72 hours later. Then, a high-volume squat and deadlift follow 72 hours afterward, then they deload. Most athletes can only sustain three max-effort workouts in a row.

The next scheduled max effort is replaced by a repetition method workout to recover from the severity of such training. Then, embark on as heavy a workload for three or four more workouts. For the squat and deadlift, this approach works for the pressing days, such as standing press or some form of bench pressing flat or angled. Remember, when you feel mentally or physically exhausted, replace the standard speed or max effort workouts with a repetition workout designed for exercising the less-fatigued muscle groups. Repetition work means lots of extensions for the back, hips, arms, and trunk.

NOTE TO READER:
Speed-Strength cycles last two or three weeks progressively, going higher in percentage and somewhat higher in volume. On Max-Effort days, the barbell exercise must change each week. For example, one week is a squat exercise, a deadlifting exercise the next, then a Goodmorning exercise, and occasionally a repetition day thrown in for overtaxed muscle recovery. These are in no particular order. Exercises must be chosen for individual goals. Again, repetition work must consist of single-joint exercises. Example exercises are back raises, glute/ham raises, triceps extensions, and the like.

Athletes have yearly plans, multi-year plans, or an Olympic-cycle plan and methodology, but one needs a timetable for developing specific systems. Westside's concept is to increase intensity while lowering the volume, making an operational plan on how fast an individual will be, how high he can jump, or how much he can lift at a particular date during the year. Then and only then will progress be noted. Is the athlete ahead or behind schedule?

The Westside system of training can check Speed-Strength every week. This is done with the three-week pendulum wave. Explosive Strength can be monitored the same as jumping progress. Maximal strength for the upper and lower body is monitored each week. Potential can be kept at more than 90 percent and sometimes even 95 percent year-long. Remember to note the four periods of training, Accumulation, Intensification, Transformation, and Delayed Transformation, are used only at the beginning of training. Then, all aspects are combined simultaneously through a yearly plan.

The Westside system prepares the athlete for the delayed transformation period or the circa-max phase Westside uses for power meets. It is a wave of the highest intensity. Hopefully, a new record of some type is set, depending on the sport. The critical Delayed Transformation phase, or the deloading phase, trains from explosive to maximal strength, covering all elements of power: coordination, fitness, flexibility, raising lactic acid, aerobic and anaerobic, and threshold barriers while increasing VO2 max. All components can and must be trained simultaneously. Delayed Transformation was adapted from track and field as well as Olympic weightlifters from the former Soviet Union.

Periodization can be a weekly, monthly, or yearly plan. This plan can lead to a four-year or an Olympic cycle. When connected to an Olympic cycle, a college athlete's sports career can be four years for improving leg and back strength, and there must be a mathematical system to follow.

Westside has used the wave system of periodization for more than 30 years with great success. It is, of course, a math problem to be addressed that combines bar speed, total volume, and precise intensity zones of a predetermined percent of a one-rep max. This, along with proper biomechanics and physics, can spell inevitable success. **One such plan follows.**

A1: The Plan: From a 400- to a 1000-Pound Squat

400-Pound Max Squat

Percent	Weight	Reps	Lifts	Band Tension	Volume
50%	200 lb.	12x2	24	25%	4,800 lb.
55%	220 lb.	12x2	24	25%	5,280-lb.
60%	240 lb.	10x2	20	25%	4,800-lb.

Bar Speed is 0.8 m/s avg.

450-Pound Max Squat

Percent	Weight	Reps	Lifts	Band Tension	Volume
50%	225 lb.	12x2	24	25%	5,400lb.
55%	250 lb.	12x2	24	25%	6,000lb.
60%	270 lb.	10x2	20	25%	5,400 lb.

Bar Speed is 0.8 m/s avg.

500-Pound Max Squat

Percent	Weight	Reps	Lifts	Band Tension	Volume
50%	250 lb.	12x2	24	25%	6,000 lb.
55%	275 lb.	12x2	24	25%	6,600 lb.
60%	300 lb.	10x2	20	25%	6,000 lb.

Bar Speed is 0.8 m/s avg.

550-Pound Max Squat

Percent	Weight	Reps	Lifts	Band Tension	Volume
50%	275 lb.	12x2	24	25%	6,600 lb.
55%	300 lb.	12x2	24	25%	7,200 lb.
60%	330 lb.	10x2	20	25%	6,600 lb.

Bar Speed is 0.8 m/s avg.

600-Pound Max Squat

Percent	Weight	Reps	Lifts	Band Tension	Volume
50%	300 lb.	12x2	24	25%	7,200 lb.
55%	330 lb.	12x2	24	25%	7,920 lb.
60%	360 lb.	10x2	20	25%	7,200 lb.

Bar Speed is 0.8 m/s avg.

650-Pound Max Squat

Percent	Weight	Reps	Lifts	Band Tension	Volume
50%	325 lb.	12x2	24	25%	7,800 lb.
55%	355 lb.	12x2	24	25%	8,520 lb.
60%	390 lb.	10x2	20	25%	7,800 lb.

Bar Speed is 0.8 m/s avg.

700-Pound Max Squat

Percent	Weight	Reps	Lifts	Band Tension	Volume
50%	350 lb.	12x2	24	25%	8,400 lb.
55%	385 lb.	12x2	24	25%	9,240 lb.
60%	420 lb.	10x2	20	25%	8,400 lb.

Bar Speed is 0.8 m/s avg.

750-Pound Max Squat

Percent	Weight	Reps	Lifts	Band Tension	Volume
50%	375 lb.	12x2	24	25%	9,000 lb.
55%	425 lb.	12x2	24	25%	10,200 lb.
60%	450 lb.	10x2	20	25%	9,000 lb.

Bar Speed is 0.8 m/s avg.

800-Pound Max Squat

Percent	Weight	Reps	Lifts	Band Tension	Volume
50%	400 lb.	12x2	24	25%	9,600 lb.
55%	440 lb.	12x2	24	25%	10,560 lb.
60%	480 lb.	10x2	20	25%	9,600 lb.

Bar Speed is 0.8 m/s avg.

850-Pound Max Squat

Percent	Weight	Reps	Lifts	Band Tension	Volume
50%	425 lb.	12x2	24	25%	10,200 lb.
55%	470 lb.	12x2	24	25%	11,280 lb.
60%	510 lb.	10x2	20	25%	10,200 lb.

Bar Speed is 0.8 m/s avg.

900-Pound Max Squat

Percent	Weight	Reps	Lifts	Band Tension	Volume
50%	450 lb.	12x2	24	25%	10,800 lb.
55%	495 lb.	12x2	24	25%	11,880 lb.
60%	540 lb.	10x2	20	25%	10,800 lb.

Bar Speed is 0.8 m/s avg.

950-Pound Max Squat

Percent	Weight	Reps	Lifts	Band Tension	Volume
50%	475 lb.	12x2	24	25%	11,400 lb.
55%	520 lb.	12x2	24	25%	12,480 lb.
60%	570 lb.	10x2	20	25%	11,400 lb.

Bar Speed is 0.8 m/s avg.

1000-Pound Max Squat

Percent	Weight	Reps	Lifts	Band Tension	Volume
50%	500 lb.	12x2	24	25%	12,000 lb.
55%	550 lb.	12x2	24	25%	13,200 lb.
60%	600 lb.	10x2	20	25%	12,000 lb.

Bar Speed is 0.8 m/s avg.

Notice the bar speed is constant, roughly .8 m/s. Secondly, it requires 600 pounds of total volume to increase the squat by 50 pounds, and the percent range is 50 percent to 60 percent. The rep range and the total number of lifts remain the same. The amount of band tension or chains is also constant. The three-week waves for some time yield the 50-pound increase by building maximal strength on Max-Effort day, 72 hours later. Then add special exercises.

By studying these graphs carefully, it can be seen how mathematics plays a prominent role in gaining strength and force production.

Let's look at the total volume for a 400-pound max squat. It is one-half of the total volume of an 800-pound max squat. A 400-pound max squat requires the person to maintain 4,800 pounds of volume; whereas, lifting 800 pounds involves 9,600 pounds of volume. This is twice as much as a 400-pound squat. A 500-pound squatter must maintain 6,000 pounds of volume. It takes 12,000 pounds to maintain a 1,000-pound squat, which is exactly twice the volume. While the goal as a coach may be to keep a squat max of

400 pounds or 700 pounds for a lineman to ensure the force development of the before-mentioned squat, the appropriate volume must be adhered to. This is a proven method of strength training, which is referred to as the Dynamic Method.

The primary goal is to develop a fast rate of force development in sports of all kinds. For those who use a Tendo unit, speed strength is the goal of 0.8 to 0.9 m/s average. Speed-Strength is trained at intermediate velocities. One must know at what rate a particular special strength is trained. Otherwise, failure will ensue while attempting to improve a special strength. These speeds can be found on Page 150 in Mel Siff's *Supertraining,* 2003.

You need to avoid accommodation in volume in a weekly plan. The special exercises will fluctuate to such an extent that accommodation is impossible. A second method is to change the total volume while training at a certain percent while using a three-week wave, and a cycle is to use a special bar at the same percent. The workload can change. Changing the percent can significantly shift the workload when doing a back squat compared to a front squat or an overhead squat. The example shows that a typical 500-pound back squatter would typically have a max front squat of 350 pounds and an overhead squat of an estimated 250 pounds. When looking at the first-week wave at 50 percent in the three different squat styles, the total volume per set of two reps would be 500 pounds, 350 pounds, and 250 pounds.

A2: Changing Total Volume

Max	Percent	Weight (pounds)	Volume
500 lb back squat	50%	250 lb.	500 lb. per set
350 lb front squat	50%	175 lb.	350 lb. per set
250 lb overhead squat	50%	125 lb.	250 lb. per set

This is the simplest way to change the volume while maintaining bar speed at the predetermined bar speed at the fixed weekly percent. For more examples, the three graphs below show using chains for a 400-pound max squat, a 600-pound max squat, and an 800-pound max squat. The bar weight remains the same for benching, but the accommodating resistance changes accordingly as maximum strength goes up.

A3: Band Bench Workout for Speed Strength

300 Max Percentages

Percentage	Weight	Reps	Band Tension	Total volume
50%	150 lb.	9x3 Reps	75 lb.	4,050 lb.
50%	150 lb.	9x3 Reps	75 lb.	4,050 lb.
50%	150 lb.	9x3 Reps	75 lb.	4,050 lb.

400 Max Percentage

Percentage	Weight	Reps	Band Tension	Total volume
50%	200 lb.	9x3 Reps	100 lb.	5,400 lb.
50%	200 lb.	9x3 Reps	100 lb.	5,400 lb.
50%	200 lb.	9x3 Reps	100 lb.	5,400 lb.

450 Max Percentage

Percentage	Weight	Reps	Band	Total volume
50%	225 lb.	9x3 Reps	125 lb.	6,000 lb.
50%	225 lb.	9x3 Reps	125 lb.	6,000 lb.
50%	225 lb.	9x3 Reps	125 lb.	6,000 lb.

These charts are guidelines for squatting and benching and variations of the Olympic lifts or the deadlift. It should teach proper planning order to control volume and intensity zones and suitable bar speed.

PERIODIZATION BY
PERCENTAGES

Westside constantly talks about the value of controlling loading by a percentage of a one-rep max. This solves the problem of overtraining or detraining. I found the importance of this after applying A.S. Prilepin's chart for loading at different percentages in *Managing the Training of Weightlifters*. He listed how many repetitions per set as well as how many lifts per workout. His findings show that if the number of lifts is vastly under or over, the training effect decreases. The subject can be thoroughly studied in *Managing the Training of Weightlifters* by NP. Laputin and V.G. Oleshko. A sound conclusion was discussed in the book A.S. Medvedev's *A System of Multi-Year Training in Weightlifting*.

At the 1964 Olympics, Leonid Zhabotinsky had won the gold medal. Zhabotinsky's volume remained the same for the next two years, although his intensity decreased. The result of this was no increase in his total. In 1967, the training intensity was raised, and once again, the totals started to rise once more. How does a sportsman increase his lift without overtraining or detraining while maintaining correct bar speed? The answer, a three-week pendulum wave for Speed-Strength development because it controls volume and intensity for one's strength level. You don't fight without a mouthpiece, you don't play football without a helmet, and you don't lift without some protective gear like a light suit with straps down or an average pair of squat briefs.

The examples below show how to raise a squat from 400 pounds to 700 pounds by adding 50 pounds each time. College sports are four years as an Olympic cycle. If strength and speed have not increased by a great deal, the athlete and coach have failed.

400-Pound Max Squat

Percent	Weight	Reps	Lifts	Band Tension	Volume
50%	200 lb.	12x2	24	25%	4,800 lb.
55%	220 lb.	12x2	24	25%	5,280 lb.
60%	240 lb.	10x2	20	25%	4,800 lb.

Bar Speed is 0.8 m/s avg.

450-Pound Max Squat

Percent	Weight	Reps	Lifts	Band Tension	Volume
50%	225 lb.	12x2	24	25%	5,400 lb.
55%	250 lb.	12x2	24	25%	6,000 lb.
60%	270 lb.	10x2	20	25%	5,400 lb.

Bar Speed is 0.8 m/s avg.

500-Pound Max Squat

Percent	Weight	Reps	Lifts	Band Tension	Volume
50%	250 lb.	12x2	24	25%	6,000 lb.
55%	275 lb.	12x2	24	25%	6,600 lb.
60%	300 lb.	10x2	20	25%	6,000 lb.

Bar Speed is 0.8 m/s avg.

550-Pound Max Squat

Percent	Weight	Reps	Lifts	Band Tension	Volume
50%	275 lb.	12x2	24	25%	6,600 lb.
55%	300 lb.	12x2	24	25%	7,200 lb.
60%	330 lb.	10x2	20	25%	6,600 lb.

Bar Speed is 0.8 m/s avg.

600-Pound Max Squat

Percent	Weight	Reps	Lifts	Band Tension	Volume
50%	300 lb.	12x2	24	25%	7,200 lb.
55%	330 lb.	12x2	24	25%	7,920 lb.
60%	360 lb.	10x2	20	25%	7,200 lb.

Bar Speed is 0.8 m/s avg.

650-Pound Max Squat

Percent	Weight	Reps	Lifts	Band Tension	Volume
50%	325 lb.	12x2	24	25%	7,800 lb.
55%	355 lb.	12x2	24	25%	8,520 lb.
60%	390 lb.	10x2	20	25%	7,800 lb.

Bar Speed is 0.8 m/s avg.

700-Pound Max Squat

Percentage	Weight	Reps	Lifts	Band Tension	Volume
50%	350 lb.	12x2	24	25%	8,400 lb.
55%	385 lb.	12x2	24	25%	9,240 lb.
60%	420 lb.	10x2	20	25%	8,400 lb.

Bar Speed is 0.8 m/s avg.

Look at the waves carefully. The bar speed remains the same during each wave regardless of the bar weight. Why is it essential irrespective of whether it is 400-pound max as a freshman or a senior's 700-pound maximum? Accommodating resistance with bands or chains must be implemented to promote accelerating strength. If strength does not increase, speed won't grow either. The athlete's volume must increase at the same intensity zones to become stronger. Each max has a correct amount of volume. Like the great Olympic champion L. Zhabotinsky found, the results will stagnate if volume stays the same. This multi-year system perfects skills as strength increases, and one should use perfect form while using moderate weights. Remember the equation *F=ma*. Three days or 72 hours later, a Max-Effort day must occur. This builds absolute strength.

Experts like A.P. Bondarchuk believe in the theory that through perfecting skills, an individual utilizes strength gains. My idea is that you increase muscular strength to perfect skills by increasing coordination. I am sure neither Bondarchuk nor I are totally correct, but this system blends both together. This system is simple mathematics.

Look at the rise in strength at 50-pound intervals, and the volume climbs 600 pounds at the same intensities. Although any pressing style — overhead press, push jerk in front, or behind the head — can use this system, let's look at the bench press. The bench waves stay at one constant percent with barbell weight. The change in resistance is made by changing the total amount of bands, chains, or weight releasers.

Examples of a Three-Week Wave

300-pound Max Bench

Percentage	Weight	Reps	Lifts	Band Tension
50%	150 lb.	9x3	27	85 lb.
50%	150 lb.	9x3	27	85 lb.
50%	150 lb.	9x3	27	85 lb.

300-pound Max Bench

Percent	Weight	Reps	Lift	Chain Weight
50%	150 lb.	9x3	27	80 lb.
50%	150 lb.	9x3	27	80 lb.
50%	150 lb.	9x3	27	80 lb.

300-pound Max Bench

Percent	Weight	Reps	Lift	Chain Weight & Band Tension
50%	150 lb.	9x3	27	80 lb.; 25 lb. at top
50%	150 lb.	9x3	27	80 lb.; 25 lb. at top
50%	150 lb.	9x3	27	80 lb.; 25 lb. at top

300-pound Max Bench
Lightened Method

Percent	Weight	Reps	Lift	Unload Weight
80%	240 lb.	9x3	27	60 lb.
80%	240 lb.	9x3	27	60 lb.
80%	240 lb.	9x3	27	60 lb.

As you can see in the four examples, it is the method of accommodating resistance to develop maximal tension throughout the entire range of motion. Often, exercise machines use a special cam with variable lever arms to apply a more significant force at the weakest point of the strength curve (V.M. Zatsiorsky). This is done with varying band tension, chain weight, or using the lightened method with different amounts of unloading in the bottom. Actual weight must be employed. Machines build muscle, not motion. Always use three different grips, none being outside the power lines.

Westside uses three types of speed pulls after speed squats.

1.   Speed pulls on the floor with bands

The math is roughly 30 percent band tension at lockout plus 50 percent bar weight of a one-rep max. A 700-pound deadlifter would use 345-pound bar weight plus 220 pounds at the top of the lift. A three-week wave would look like this:

Wide Sumo on Floor				
Week	Weight	Reps	Sets	Band Tension
1	345 lb.	3	10	220 lb.
2	345 lb.	3	8	220 lb.
3	345 lb.	3	6	220 lb.

Conventional Rack Pulls with Bands				
Week	Weight	Reps	Sets	Band Tension
4	345 lb.	2	10	250 lb.
5	345 lb.	2	8	250 lb.
6	345 lb.	2	6	250 lb.

Close Sumo on Floor				
Week	Weight	Reps	Sets	Band Tension
7	345 lb.	1	10	280 lb.
8	345 lb.	1	8	280 lb.
9	345 lb.	1	6	280 lb.

Conventional Rack Pulls				
Week	Weight	Reps	Sets	Band Tension
10	315 lb.	3	10	350 lb.
11	315 lb.	3	8	350 lb.
12	315 lb.	3	6	350 lb.

2.   Ultra-wide sumo deadlifts with bar weight

Ultra-Wide Sumo with Barbell weight			
Week	Weight	Reps	Sets
13	500 lb.	3	10
14	500 lb.	3	8
15	500 lb.	3	6

Notice how a three-week wave is constantly altered to avoid accommodation. The weight may vary, or the stance may change from sumo to conventional to ultra-wide sumo to rack pulls.

3.   Box deadlifts

Discussed are box deadlifts. I suggest placing the bar on mats to raise the elevation of the barbell. This maintains the feel of the mechanics of the bar. The band tension also changes each cycle or on the fourth week. The loading graphs are based on a 700-pound-max deadlift. All one needs is to reduce the amount of bar weight and band tension by 50 percent.

Wide Sumo on Floor 350-pound Deadlift				
Week	Weight	Reps	Sets	Band Tension
1	175 lb.	3	10	110 lb.
2	175 lb.	3	8	110 lb.
3	175 lb.	3	6	110 lb.

Conventional Rack Pull with Bands				
Week	Weight	Reps	Sets	Band Tension
4	175 lb.	2	10	125 lb.
5	175 lb.	2	8	125 lb.
6	175 lb.	2	6	125 lb.

Close Sumo on Floor				
Week	Weight	Reps	Sets	Band Tension
7	175 lb.	1	10	140lb.
8	175 lb.	1	8	140 lb.
9	175 lb.	1	6	140 lb.

Conventional Rack Pull				
Week	Weight	Reps	Sets	Band Tension
10	160 lb.	3	10	175 lb.
11	160 lb.	3	8	175 lb.
12	160 lb.	3	6	175 lb.

Ultra-Wide Sumo with Barbell weight			
Week	Weight	Reps	Sets
13	250 lb.	3	10
14	250 lb.	3	8
15	250 lb.	3	6

Again, note that each three-week wave is somehow different. It may be the bar weight, it can be band tension, or it could be altered by a different stance or how far the bar is off the floor. Using a power rack or placing plates on rubber mats, one can also stand on a 2-inch or 4-inch box. A 350-pound deadlift is half or 50 percent of the volume of a 700-pound deadlift.

Mathematics is an essential part of weight lifting because a lifter must control the total volume of a training session—the intensity zones or what percent of a one-rep max must also be considered. As graphs in this text show, the volume must be highest on speed strength day while the intensities are moderately low — 50 percent to 80 percent. The max effort day would require the intensity zone to possibly be 100 percent plus, allowing the volume to be as low as 35 percent to 50 percent. The loading for power cleans, and power snatches without bands or chains must also be regulated.

Top weight lifters must use various exercises, not just power cleans and power snatches but the classical clean, jerk, and snatch. More than 50 percent of all training must be comprised of special exercises such as back raises, belt squats, inverse curls, box jumps, Reverse Hypers®, Goodmornings, a wide variety of pulls, squats, jerks, and presses.

The Soviets were experts in calculating volume and intensities. Men like A.S. Prilepin, A.D. Ermakov and N.S. Atanasov provided studies in *Managing and Training of Weightlifters* that determined how many snatches and clean jerks were to be done in a single workout and how many reps and sets, and at what percent they should be monitored. Although my observations are very close to these, I find it is crucial to train optimally, not maximally or minimally. Plus, the percents for weight lifting are kept five percent lower than their recommendation. The data from 1975 by A.D. Ermakov and N.S. Atansov in *Managing and Training of Weightlifters* found roughly 50 percent of the lifts fell between 75 percent and 85 percent. While it is fully recognized this is where speed strength is developed, many did not grow up doing weight lifting. I propose performing five percent less on each three-week wave.

Example:

300-pound Power Clean				
Week	Percent	Reps	Sets	Lifts
1	70%	3	6	18
2	75%	3	6	18
3	80%	3	4	12

This workout can be done after Friday's speed squat workout. Rest between sets for about 90 seconds. This requires good GPP. After all, you are an athlete, right?

250-pound Power Snatch				
Week	Percent	Reps	Sets	Lifts
1	70%	3	6	18
2	75%	3	6	18
3	80%	3	4	12

This workout can follow a max effort workout on Monday. First, do a max exercise: low box squats, overhead squat, good mornings, box pulls, rack pulls, heavy sled pulls for 60 yards. Rest 90 seconds. After a heavy lift, a clean or snatch feels lighter and faster. Add variety like band tension of different amounts. I give credit to three great men: Ermakov, Atanasov, and Prilephin's in *Managing and Training of Weightlifters*, and Verkhoshansky and Medvedev in *A System of Multi-Year Training in Weightlifting*, for not only guiding my career from 1983 but undoubtedly saving my lifting career. I have slightly modified the volume and intensity by using somewhat lighter lifts. One reason is due to a lesser background in GPP and physical preparedness, and second, we use a lot of powerlifting exercises.

A lifter must wave back down after a three-week wave but also change something, at least slightly. Vary the amount of bar weight, band tension, chains, weight, box height, pin height, or bars to avoid accommodation. The speed day volume will be the highest while intensity will be at a low 40 percent to moderate 80 percent. Seventy-two hours later on max effort day requires the intensity to be a max of that particular day, hopefully meaning a near all-time max or an all-time max on some special exercise. It is gaining strength in the right special exercises that brings forth the next personal best in a clean or snatch or jerk.

If an individual fully understands the process or percents, he will never overtrain or undertrain. He needs to alternate weak muscle groups to prevent injuries and constantly progress until he reaches his sport's potential. Use three, three-week waves before trying a new max. In the beginning, progress is easy, but as an individual starts to lift weights close to his potential as only a handful have, it becomes more difficult. It's lonely at the top.

For the weightlifter, it is most important to raise absolute strength to overcome larger loads; to become faster is secondary to power. This is a common misconception of weightlifting coaches in the United States. After all, world record weights move slower than training weights. An athlete must use the optimal weight for his strength. The amount of work and rest must be monitored as well as movement tempo. Weight lifting requires a great deal of speed and strength. While speed is a significant factor, strength is necessary to lift with speed to develop quick strength.

As strength and speed at each percent increase, an individual achieves a new max to work from. This yields a more significant training volume. Remember, the chart shows how a 400-max squat volume is 4,800 pounds and how a 500-max squat requires 6,000 pounds of volume. For every 50 pounds gained in a max squat, a rise in the volume of 600 pounds will be factored in at the same 50 percent to 60 percent. There is much to consider when perfecting form: GPP, recovery methods, relaxation, and above all, a selection of the correct special exercises for the individual. Mental, physical, and emotional maturity needs to be considered. Many require a plan. This is a plan for an individual's current strength level and how to raise it correctly. The amount of rest between sets must be a factor because this can be critical for recovery. The percent of a one-rep max and the volume the training plan calls for is imperative. This is the interval method, much like track athletes use.

With small weights that football players use for speed development, the rest between sets represent most football plays, four to seven seconds. An individual should and must recover in 40 seconds for 12 sets of two reps. For explosive strength development, 24 sets of two reps can be performed with 40-second intervals, which builds explosive strength in a fatigued state and represents training at 70 percent to 85 percent. The rest must be 60 seconds to 90 seconds between sets. Max effort work can require two to four minutes rest between singles, dependent on the athlete's level of physical preparedness.

A.S. Prilepin discovered and shared in *Managing and Training of Weightlifters* that too many reps per set can change a reduction in force development. It is best to perform high sets and low reps for recovery. The high rep sets should only include special exercises for individual muscles. While his recommendation was with weights at 70 percent to 90 percent, I concluded 40 percent to 60 percent, and the results were the same. If one watches a ball bounce with every preceding bounce, the rebound has less height. Why? It's due to the loss of kinetic energy.

The human body works similarly with the expenditure of kinetic energy in soft tissue and muscle fatigue. Repetitions range for explosive strength or explosive power. Starting strength is inherited due to the amount or ratio of fast and slow-twitch muscle fiber in the muscle. The same holds true for absolute strength, where one lifts maximum weight with no time limit. After years of following the guidelines set forth by AS Prilepin, AD Ermakov, NS Atanasov, and many other sports experts from the former Soviet Union, I have considered my own 50 years of experience. Here are my suggestions for planning sets, reps per workout at a predetermined intensity zone for any athlete after three years of general preparation.

If bar speed is reduced, the set must be stopped because of a power reduction. Pay close attention to the minimal and maximal total reps and amount of lifts per workout. For most, the optimal number of lifts is more beneficial.

Percent	Reps	Lifts
40%	4-8	36
50%	3-6	36
60%	3-6	30
70%	3-6	18
80%	2-4	15
90%	1-2	4-10

If you are significantly above or below the optimal number, the training effects are diminished. Here are my recommendations.

40% no less than 24 and no more than 48
50% no less than 24 and no more than 48
60% no less than 20 and no more than 40
70% no less than 12 and no more than 24
80% no less than 10 and no more than 20
90% no less than 4 and no more than 10

HOW TO CHANGE THE VOLUME AT THE SAME INTENSITY ZONE

Your three maxes for a front squat, safety-squat bar, and of course, a regular-squat bar max. Here is how:

500-pound Max
Front Squat

Week	Percent	Weight	Reps	Lift	Volume
1	50%	250 lb.	12x2	24	6,000 lb.
2	55%	275 lb.	12x2	24	6,600 lb.
3	60%	300 lb.	10x2	20	6,000 lb.

Bar Speed is .8 m/s

600-pound Max
Safety Squat Bar

Week	Percent	Weight	Reps	Lift	Volume
1	50%	300 lb.	12x2	24	7,200 lb
2	55%	330 lb.	12x2	24	7,920 lb.
3	60%	360 lb.	10x2	20	7,200 lb.

Bar Speed is .8 m/s

700-pound Max
Regular Squat Bar

Week	Percent	Weight	Reps	Lift	Volume
1	50%	350 lb.	12x2	24	8,400 lb.
2	55%	385 lb.	12x2	24	9,240 lb.
3	60%	420 lb.	10x2	20	8,400 lb.

Bar Speed is .8 m/s

Pay close attention to these graphs for continued progress in classical barbell lifts, including the following: Olympic weightlifting lifts, powerlifting lifts, special squats, good mornings, pull, and pressing exercises. However, by combining mathematics, physics, and biomechanics, your true potential can be reached.

FIGURE 3.1
RATIO OF SPECIAL EXERCISE TO BARBELL EXERCISES

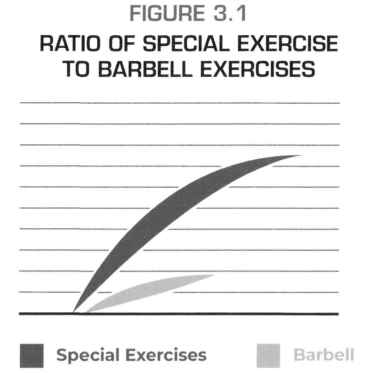

■ Special Exercises   ■ Barbell

Figure 3: As you can see in Figure 3, the barbell and classical lifts ratio are 20 percent barbell exercises and 80 percent special exercises. This is proven by the research done at Westside Barbell by Joe Lasko on powerlifts and Olympic weightlifting and track and field. Because athletes are built biomechanically differently, it can be dangerous to perform high repetition barbell lifts, as the weakest component of the human can become fatigued and sustain injuries. It is much safer to do special exercises directed to a particular muscle group that may be lacking.

Circa Max

Max Weight	Bar Weight	Weight Percent	Band Tension	Band Percent
800 lb.	500 lb.	62%	375 lb.	47%
850 lb.	550 lb.	61%	375 lb.	44%
900 lb.	600 lb.	66%	375 lb.	42%
950 lb.	650 lb.	68%	375 lb.	39%
1000 lb.	600 lb.	60%	440 lb.	44%
1050 lb.	650 lb.	62%	440 lb.	42%
1100 lb.	700 lb.	64%	440 lb.	40%
1150 lb.	750 lb.	65%	440 lb.	38%

Delayed Transformation Connecting Circa-Max Phase

The results at the contest are, of course, of most importance. It requires two proven methods of periodization. First, Delayed Transformation is a period where you reduce the amount of volume and reduce the intensity zone somewhat to induce the highest level of sporting skill at contest time. It was brought about through track and field and Olympic weightlifting from the former Soviet Union. It starts at 35 days out from the contest date for squat training, and you perform roughly 50 percent sets for the optimal amounts of sets and lifts. The same is true for 28 days out of your contest.

It is interrupted at 21 days. Westside lifters do a new or all-time record on a box squat. See the circa-max chart above and circa-max, meaning near max. A circa-max phase is performed with weights in the range of 90 percent to 97 percent if a one-rep max. The number of lifts at those percentages are four minimal, seven optimal, and ten maximal. Westside uses the optimal method, utilizing seven lifts on Circa-Max day.

An 800-pound squatter after a warm-up performs the following:

330 pounds bar weight x 2 reps + 375 pounds band tension

370 pounds bar weight x 2 reps + 375 pounds band tension

420 pounds bar weight x 1 rep + 375 pounds band tension

470 pounds bar weight x 1 rep + 375 pounds band tension

PR 510 pounds bar weight x 1 rep + 375 pounds band tension

If an athlete can perform this weight and if the box height is correct (parallel and good form), he will break a new squat record. During the second week of Circa-Max, the lifter will work up to approximately 370 pounds for a single.

This concludes the circa-max phase. It represents 21 days out and 14 days out. Now more recovery time is needed. Seven days out, large men (275 pounds and up) will not squat but do only special exercises. Two hundred forty-two-pound athletes and lighter can squat light. Three hundred and thirty pounds at 2 x 2 with no band tension, or if you prefer 140 pounds of band tension, is an example.

As you see, to assure all three lifts are at their max on contest day, Westside divides the delayed transformation phase into two parts: part one with extreme stimulus at 21 days out, then part two back to the Delayed Transformation through 14 days out. Refer to chart 3.1 to explain our combination method training by using bands on and bar weight.

This chart is the combined efforts of 75 men who have officially squatted 800 pounds up to 1,270 pounds. Look carefully at the bar weight percentages and the band tension percentages. As a lifter progresses from 800 pounds to 950 pounds, the bar percentage goes from 62 percent up to 68 percent, causing the band tension to go from 47 percent to 39 percent. This means the bar percent goes up 6 percent while the band tension goes down 8 percent.

Let it be noted that at 1,000 pounds to 1,150 pounds, the bar percent goes up five percent while the band tension goes down six percent. I am asked about scientific studies; no one has such a study as Westside with world-class strength athletes. Our conclusions are based on more than twenty years of experiments and experience.

"If you run with
the lame, you will
develop a limp."
—Louie Simmons

CONJUGATE FOR GPP

GENERAL PHYSICAL PREPAREDNESS

ATHLETIC SUCCESS PYRAMID

SPP
Special Physical Preparedness

PF
Physical Fitness

GPP
General Preparedness Physical

Think about the idea that a pyramid is only as tall as its base, and let's talk about General Physical Preparedness or GPP. Think of GPP as the base of your Athletic Success Pyramid. To be successful, you need a solid base of GPP and then equal amounts of PF and SPP.

Even GPP exercises must be rotated to be effective. To recover from high-volume workouts that are done at Westside, a high level of preparedness is necessary. We ask our bodies to constantly recover from workout to workout.

Four large high-volume workouts, at least four small special workouts a week, must be completed without diminishing performance.

ACCUMULATION PHASE

The Accumulation Phase prepares the lifter as they begin their journey with Westside. Westside runs one Accumulation Phase and never needs to do it again as the athlete advances their training. The training must be severe to cause a change in the adaptation that forces the athlete to move on to a higher-volume activity. This is essential for attaining the highest level of sports excellence.

For the weightlifter or powerlifters, there is not much need to work on raising the VO2 maximum. After 12 to 18 months of training, the athlete's VO2 max will be at its highest limit. There is no need to push it. The expected VO2 maximum has stayed constant since the 1940s, yet running times have continued to improve. By adding Strength-Endurance training, athletes have added muscular endurance. GPP was first intended for the early stages of sports training to provide a well-rounded program to improve all aspects of physical qualities. Balanced fitness includes the physical attributes of speed, strength, flexibility, and special endurance.

GPP FOR THE
WEIGHTLIFTER OR
POWERLIFTER

An athlete must start with shortening rest intervals over time. And do not use the exact time between sets. Vary the rest times.

Hamstrings

To execute the Conjugate System, the strength athlete should rotate calf-ham-glute raises after three to six workouts with inverse curls for three to six exercises and then to a standard leg curl machine. Reverse Hypers TM is also an excellent choice for rotation, then back to the calf-ham-glute raises. Constantly rotate the exercises to avoid accommodation while also increasing the strength of your hamstrings.

Triceps

Now let's look at Triceps. Use dumbbell rollbacks for a few workouts, then EZ curl-bar extensions. Next, you could do elbows out to the side or Williams Extensions. Or, it could be straight bar extensions with French Presses next. You can rotate to J.M. Presses for your triceps, too.

As you can see, all these exercises work, but you must change the variety to constantly build stronger triceps.

Delts

When training your delts, do dumbbell front raises and when you feel the need, go to a plate raise. Cables can also be used with a power rack at three feet or more height with straight legs or bent legs.

Build the front delts. Side and rear delts can be trained with cables, rubber bands, dumbbells, or a pec deck in reverse.

Pressing

The Conjugate System can work for all special strengths for pressing. Incline, decline, seated, standing, flat bench with dumbbells, or a barbell. I would box squat on a 17-, 15-, 13-, 12-, or 10-inch box or deadlift standing on a four-, two-, or five-inch box Sumo or conventional style, using bent legs or stiff legs. You can use 220 to 280 pounds of band tension. Or in a Power Rack at three or more height. Straight-legged or bent-legged Goodmornings work as well.

The three-week waves change the percent each week. An example is 75 percent the first week, 80 percent the second week, and 85 percent the third week, then drop back to 75 percent and start the three-week wave over again.

When doing special barbell exercises, like a rack pull or a Goodmorning, always think of it as part of a classical lift. Every single-joint activity, such as Reverse Hypers, acts as if you are locking out a deadlift or a back extension. It should duplicate the lockout at the top of a deadlift.

A great example of GPP that closely resembles SPP (specific physical preparation) is the box squat. Westside only box squats in training but has had nine men who have held all-time world records in the squat.

GPP FOR
FOOTBALL

A football game only has seven to nine minutes of playing time for the offense or the defense, but they practice hours and hours on all types of plays, drills, and the weight room. All the plays and drills resemble a football play. Lots of conditioning is directed at a football play. Everything that is done in practice is geared at football. This is GPP that must look like SPP to be successful.

GPP FOR
COMBAT SPORTS

For an MMA fighter, GPP can be training one discipline of fighting. It could be Maui Thai, Judo, Jujitsu, Boxing, or Grappling when just doing one fighting style. Training could include hitting all combat bags like a Hy bag, speed bag, a double-end bag, or a ground and pound bag. The bags can not be trained all at once, but they would pick one or two bags to work on each day.

Focus pads are used for combinations and building timing and coordination.

The MMA fighter also must work on many kicks. In this regard, an adage often heard that it is better to practice one kick 1,000 times than 1,000 kicks one time. They are mostly done without actual sparring. In fact, today, many fighters don't spar much at all to save their bodies and careers.

The weight training must be at a fast pace, just like a fight. You hit or kick a bag like it is your adversary at fight time. Pull or push a weight sled like it is at the end of a fight, and you are behind on points.

The point is that during your training, you must do everything like you are in a fight or in a game or in a lifting contest. But for you to excel, most everything in your training must be close in structure to your sport.

GPP FOR THE
SPRINTER

Explosive weight training has a profound effect on sprinting. In a 1999 research project, Leena Paavolainen reduced her participants' running by 32 percent and replaced running with explosive weight training. The training included Plyometrics to improve maximal ground force with a reduction in ground contact. The result was enhanced sprinting times, or actually, improved times for any length of a race.

This is the Conjugate System aimed at improving the runner's strength to cause faster speeds. The speed achievements were accomplished without improvement in VO2 max. In addition to conventional weight exercises, other exercises included static and dynamic stretching, pressing of all types, deadlifts with Plyometrics, and leg lifts and obliques. The deadlifts were Sumo, close-stance with a close grip or snatch-grip. They used no Olympic lifts. Olympic lifts do not build explosive strength by themselves, but only at 30 percent to 40 percent, where velocity training will build explosive power with any barbell or special single-joint exercise.

According to Thomas Kurz, you must learn to do fast movements and improve endurance to increase coordination and agility as you run, jump, or climb while playing various sports and games. Everything must be rotated to avoid the Law of Accommodation.

You should interconnect GPP and SPP to improve sports performance with exercises that provide overall conditioning and enhance the performance of a single muscle group. All sports should use reactive methods, meaning Plyometric Methods, which will increase explosive strength and reactive ability.

Remember, it does no good to be strong in the wrong exercises. Continually evaluate your past and current training and know what works and what does not.

" I may not have invented toilet paper, but I am smart enough to use it."
—Louie Simmons

SPECIAL DEVICES FOR CONJUGATE TRAINING

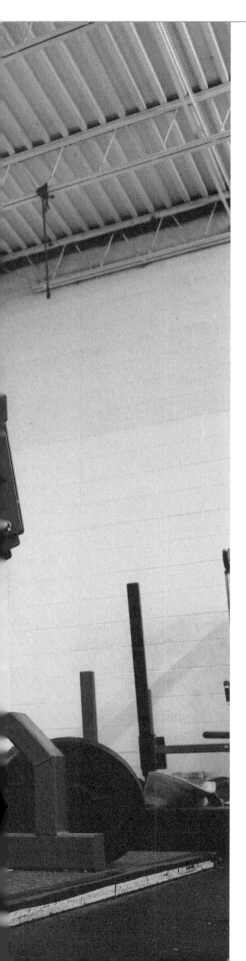

If an athlete wants to improve his or her performance, they must use various special exercises. Keep in mind, however, that the USA weight lifters train with a minimum of training aids. A glute-ham bench and rubber plates are the extents of their training. Compare that to the Chinese who have a Reverse Hyper, Glute-Ham Bench, Power Rack, Bands, and perform many bodybuilding exercises at the end of their workouts. Think of it ... at least two bodybuilding exercises after each workout; when their backs are exhausted, they perform belt squats. That is why the Chinese rule the Olympic lifting world.

If you, too, want to be successful, just look on the sports market, and you will find an endless list of machines and other apparatus to buy for your training.

Westside athletes rotate among several special bars for pressing, squatting, and Goodmornings. On M-E day, the workouts consist of many special barbell exercises for 20 percent of the volume, with the remaining 80 percent being small special exercises.

But why rotate exercises? My good friend Jimmy Seitzer always went to various gyms and then trained with the Westside guys. He was a former Mr. USA, plus third and fifth place winner. I asked Jimmy why he had to go to so many gyms. Jimmy would tell me that I did not understand. He said the machines are always slightly different and hit the muscles at different angles for a better muscular result. Jimmy was right. By making a slight change, he avoided the Law of Accommodation. And, this is why Westside changes special bars and machines when needed.

On M-E day, the bar is rotated each week, and on Speed-Strength day, every fourth week at 75 percent to 85 percent.

BARS LIST

1.	Bulldog Squat Bar	11.	Belt Squat Machine
2.	Bulldog Deadlift Bar	12.	Overhead Squat Bar
3.	Bulldog Bench Press bar	13.	Manta Ray Bar
4.	Bow Bar	14.	Zercher Squat Bar
5.	Three-inch Camber Bar	15.	Arch Bar
6.	Five-inch Camber Bar	16.	Football Bar
7.	14-inch Camber Bar	17.	Tee Bar
8.	Safety Squat Bar	18.	Band Bar
9.	Front Squat Bar	19.	EZ Curl Bar
10.	Mars Bar	20.	Earthquake Bar

A total of 20 special bars.

Why Switch Bars?

The lifter's spine length will never change, making it difficult to distribute the muscular loads of different muscles. But, by changing a bulldog squat for a Manta Ray, where the bar is positioned about two inches above the top of the shoulder, it makes the lift into the ultra-Olympic-style squat.

We know how different a back squat is from a front squat or a safety squat bar squat when compared to a Zercher squat. Every bar will cause the lifter to stress the muscles differently.

For pressing exercises, a five-inch camber bar provides five inches greater range of motion. Even a close-grip is much different than a wide-grip bench. A seated front press is quite different from a seated-behind-the-head press. Any variety of pressing will avoid the Law of Accommodation and slows progress to be continuous. This allows the athlete to have numerous records to break, which leads to a positive mindset.

SPECIAL MACHINES LIST

1.	Calf-ham-glute machine	13.	Mono-Lift
2.	Reverse HyperR*	14.	Bands
3.	Inverse Curl	15.	Chains
4.	Hip Quad	16.	Static Dynamic Device
5.	Leg Press	17.	Isometrics
6.	Ply-O-Swing	18.	Hack Squat
7.	Belt Squat	19.	Leg Extensions
8.	K Box	20.	Leg Curl
9.	Chest-Support Row	21.	Power Rack
10.	Lat Pulldown	22.	Weight Sled
11.	Dips	23.	Wheelbarrow
12.	Pushups		

* The Reverse Hyper™ has four different models from which to choose and rotate. There are too many to list.

But, let's look at some rotations for the low back, hamstrings, and glutes, and let's start with rotating Westside's Reverse Hypers.

A Strap Model will work the glutes and upper hamstrings very heavily. A Roller Model will place most of the work on the spinal erectors by making the stress on the spinal erectors first, then the glutes and the hamstrings. A Bent Pendulum model will place most of the load on the lower back and upper hamstrings, with the pendulum pulling the athlete's legs 19 inches under the machine for more range of motion and isolating the lower back. A Dual Pendulum model can make it possible to train one side at a time, much like running or swimming.

All models of the Reverse Hyper are open-chain machines. This means no legs or hands are in contact. Each model works somewhat differently to avoid the Law of Accommodation.

To constantly raise the strength of the hamstrings, rotate from a calf-ham-glute raise, after the positive training effect no longer exists, about three to six workouts, exchange it for inverse curls. The Law of Accommodation will always become a negative aspect of training. When this occurs, you must rotate to a second, single-joint exercise. Standard leg curls can be added along with standing leg curls for a short three to six workout cycle. These are only two examples of the Conjugate System.

There are many exercises to rotate, including for the upper body. Let's look at rotating the tricep exercises.

The athlete may choose tricep rollbacks for a short time; then, a second exercise could be EZ Curl Bar French Press for three to six workouts. Next, the Williams Tricep with Elbow Out to the Sides on an Incline. J.M Presses or Straight Bar Extensions can be added to the program.

The particular exercises above are used after a Speed-Strength or Explosive-Strength training, or also on M-E Day.

M-E WORKOUTS

Science has proven that if you use a barbell or dumbbell exercise above 90 percent for three weeks, you will stop making much progress due to accommodation. Let's review once again what can be done to avoid the problem.

Westside trains for a new personal record each week with a new personal record at over a 92 percent rate. The technique is to switch to a new barbell lift each week.

Power walking with a sled can be rotated with pushing and pulling a wheelbarrow. For maximum strength, go 60 meters a trip. For conditioning, a trip of one or two miles can be made. Add a weight vest, ankle weights, or Kettlebells to change the effort per trip.

Jumping

Depth jumps should be done twice a week. Twenty-four jumps for novice and 40 twice a week for the more advanced. The depth jumps are coupled with a rebound and a maximum jump for building explosive power, mainly on a 20-inch box. When the box height is higher, the absorption phase will take too long to be Plyometric. Depth drops are done on a much higher box without a rebound for building maximal strength.

M-E Conjugate

When doing Goodmornings, a rotation could be Rack-Pin Goodmornings with a limited range of motion and movement. The following workout can be done with an arched back with a slightly greater range of motion. Next, perform a Bend-Over Goodmorning where the range of motion can reach parallel to the platform.

Let's look at training the deadlift in two methods. First, Rack Pulls. At Westside, Pin 3 will have the plates six and one-half inches off the platform. A second M-E workout can be on Pin 2 with the plates four and one-half inches off the platform. A third workout can be Pin 1. Now, the plates are two and one-half inches off the platform. It is common to do two pins in one workout but never repeat the same Pin Pull for two weeks.

You can do the same for Box Deadlifts. Pull off a four-inch box or a two-inch box. For more motion, build a box to about five inches where the bar is touching the top of the foot. A radical deadlift is to stand on a 10-inch box and deadlift with a Five-Inch Camber Bar. The hands are now four inches below your feet.

Rack pulls. Box deadlifts. Different boxes for box squatting. Benches of all angles. Many different bars. Dumbbells. Weight Sled. Wheelbarrow walking. Box jumping. Even power gear like single-ply or double-ply briefs. Close stance, wide stance, benching with three grips. This is what it takes to utilize the Conjugate System of training. Even changing your weight class must be considered to achieve new records.

The body is constantly changing, and the athlete must continuously adjust the exercises and program to excel at any sport. Night into day, summer to fall, fall to winter, and winter to spring, and the rotation goes on just like the Conjugate System.

M-E for Upper Body Workouts

If you want to bench big, you have to do more than flat-bench. You can do the workouts in any sequence. Consider incline press, rack pin presses, decline presses, seated presses, dumbbell workouts about every third or fourth week.

Westside will do two M-E lifts in one workout. Remember, an M-E workout should be separated by 72 hours. A maximal effort is one rep. If you do two or three reps, this is the Method of Heavy Effort. All barbell M-E lifts can be done with a regular bench bar, or you can use a Football Bar, Arch Bar, or a variety of camber bars, including three or five-inch cambers.

Conjugate for Olympic Lifting

The Olympic lifter has nearly 100 workouts to choose from. They can be found in *Supertraining* or *Fundamentals of Special Strength*. Y.V. Verkhoshansky's book titled *Fundamentals of Special Strength Training in Sport* also has the same 100 workouts created by A. N. Medvedev. Just pick six to 10 workouts and rotate them.

"Don't train maximally,
never train minimally,
always train OPTIMALLY."
—Louie Simmons

MAXIMAL EFFORT WORKOUTS

About Maximal Effort (M-E) Workouts

Westside has two M-E workouts a week. One is for pressing, and one is for squatting, deadlifting, or the snatch and clean and jerk. They are separated from an Explosive or Speed-Strength workout by 72 hours for total recovery.

The M-E Method is superior to all other training methods for improving both intramuscular and intermuscular coordination. The muscles and Central Nervous System (CNS) adapt only to the load placed on them.

The Bulgarian weightlifting team did M-E workouts based daily. Their intensity average was much higher than all of their competitors. Even daily, the weight would be close to 92 percent to 100 percent-plus.

The Westside M-E Method calls for setting an all-time record at all M-E workouts with two M-E exercises on the same training day. One is at 90 percent, 95 percent, or 100 percent-plus. Following this regiment, an all-time record is made over 92 percent of the time. This accounts for six lifts over 92 percent twice a week. One is for pressing and the other for squats and pulls.

After M-E work with a barbell, two to four small special exercises are done.

Several side effects can result from M-E work, but all can be eliminated by rotating the barbell lift each week. M-E work is not planned long-term because this alone can cause anxiety or depression. At Westside, it is scheduled for that day during a 6 am breakfast.

Remember, strength is truly measured not by weight but by velocity. Know that when an athlete lifts a limit weight, movement velocity will be at its ultimate value and remain nearly constant. As its acceleration reaches near zero, the force applied is close to equal to the weight of the object lifted.

In M-E training, rotation is paramount. Side effects will be eliminated with workout rotation.

M-E WORKOUTS LIST

In the list of M-E workouts for powerlifters, only one M-E lift will be shown with a group of small special exercises per workout. Abs must be worked each session. A second small workout should be done eight to 12 hours later on a lagging muscle group.

1. **Low Box Squat to New Max**
   a. Calf-Ham-Glute Raise
   b. Bend-Over Rows
   c. Standing Hamstrings
   d. Reverse Hyper ™

2. **Pin 3 Rack Pulls**
   a. Calf-Ham-Glute Raise
   b. Bend-Over Rows
   c. Standing Leg Curl
   d. Reverse Hyper

3. **Sumo Deadlift on Four-Inch Box**
   a. Inverse Curl
   b. Low Pulley Rows
   c. Light Goodmorning with 8 to 15 reps
   d. Reverse Hyper

4. **Box Squat Plus 375 pounds of Band**
   a. Inverse Curl
   b. Chest-Supported Rows
   c. Light Goodmornings
   d. Reverse Hyper

5. **Ultra-Wide Sumo Deadlift**
   a. Back Raise
   b. Calf-Ham-Glute Raise
   c. Upper Body Weight-Sled Work
   d. Reverse Hyper

6. **Pin 1 Rack Pull**
   a. Back Raise
   b. Ply O Swing
   c. Maximal Recruiter machine, the MR-19
   d. Reverse Hyper

7. **5 Rep Max Goodmorning**
   a. Weight Sled 10 trips, 60 meters
   b. Calf-Ham-Glute Raise
   c. MR-19
   d. Reverse Hyper

8. **Straight-Leg Sumo Deadlift**
   a. Weight Sled 10 Trips, 60 Meters
   b. Calf-Glute-Ham Raise
   c. Standing Leg Curl
   d. Reverse Hyper

9. **700-Pound Band Tension Plus Barbell Weight**
   a. Arched-Back Goodmorning Light
   b. Inverse Curl
   c. Reverse Hyper

10. **Stand on Four-Inch Box Close-Stance Deadlift**
    a. Arched Back Goodmorning Light
    b. High-Pull with Snatch Grip
    c. 45 Degree Back Raise
    d. Reverse Hyper

11. **Static Dynamic Developer Six Positions**
    a. High Pull Close Grip
    b. Barbell Rows
    c. Heavy Band Leg Curl
    d. Reverse Hyper

12. **Static Dynamic Developer Six Positions**
    a. Heavy Belt Squat
    b. Barbell Row
    c. Heavy Band Curl
    d. Reverse Hyper

13. **Belt Squat Power Clean**
    a. Walk-in Belt Squat two minutes, three sets
    b. Calf-Ham-Glute Raise
    c. Reverse Hyper

14. **Sumo Deadlift Plus 280 Pounds of Bands**

    a. Ply-O-Swing
    b. Inverse Curl
    c. Dumbbell Rows
    d. Reverse Hyper

15. **Pin 3 Rack Pull with 350 Pounds Plus Barbell Weight**
    a. Low Box Squat 12-Inch or Lower, Close Stance
    b. Inverse Curl
    c. Back Raise
    d. Reverse Hyper

16. **Max Box Squat Parallel with Just Barbell Weight**
    a. Low Box Squat 12-Inch or Lower, Wide Stance
    b. Standing Leg Curl
    c. Back Raise
    d. Reverse Hyper

This is a small list, but the available workouts are endless. With the many rack pins, boxes for squatting and deadlifting, bars, and the countless amounts of band tension and chain weights to choose from, you must find the group to use that works best for you.

Remember to choose an M-E workout the morning of your session. Deciding on the same day will remove any anxiety you may have with a difficult lift. If you plan a week ahead, you can develop anxiety for the entire week due to poor performance in that lift. By choosing the exercises the morning of the workout, there is no time for fear to form.

Also, remember to do two M-E lifts in one workout.

NOTE:
Note: Abs and Reverse Hypers are always done on each training day. This includes pressing workouts and small special workouts.

BENCH PRESS M-E WORKOUTS

1. **Option One**
   a. Flat Bench for One Rep Max (1RM) with Straight Bar
   b. Drop Weight Down for Rep Personal Record (PR)
   c. J.M Press
   d. Plate Raises
   e. Bent-Over Rows with Barbell
   f. Banded Tricep pushdowns
   g. Banded Force Pulls

2. **Option Two**
   a. Decline Bench for 1RM
   b. Skull Crushers with EZ Curl Bar
   c. One-Arm Shoulder Press
   d. Lat Pull Down
   e. Williamson Press

3. **Option Three**
   a. Incline Press for 1RM with Straight Bar
   b. JM Press with Football Bar
   c. Straight Weight Pin Presses with Straight Bar
   d. Upright Row Off Cable Machine
   e. Decline Dumbbell Rollbacks Superset with Banded Push-Downs
   f. Chest-Supported Row

4. **Option Four**
   a. Flat Bench with Monster Minis and Straight Bar 1RM
   b. Heavy Dumbbell Rollbacks Off Floor
   c. Standing Bradford Press
   d. Hammer Strength Rows (turn facing pad with elbows on rails)
   e. One-Arm Dumbbell Row
   f. Banded Tricep Push-Downs to Failure

5. **Option Five**
   a. Seated Shoulder Press Off of a Pin
   b. Heavy Decline Dumbbell Press
   c. Power Clean
   d. Pin JM Presses with Cambered Bar
   e. Seal Tow with Dumbbell or Straight Bar
   f. Reverse Fly on Pec Deck
   g. Shrugs on Wheelbarrow

6. **Option Six**
   a. Floor Press Straight Weight
   b. Incline Williamson Press
   c. Seated Bradford Press
   d. Skull Crusher with EZ Bar with Mini Attached
   e. Lat Pull-Down Ultra-Wide Grip
   f. Dumbbell Raises

7. **Option Seven**
   a. Cambered Bench Bar with Chain or Band, Flat Bench
   b. Iso Holds on Flat Bench with Straight Weight
   c. Dumbbell Roll-Backs, Slight Incline
   d. Chest-Supported Row
   e. JM Press Straight Bar to Failure
   f. Push-Ups Until Failure

8. **Option Eight**
   a. Standing/Incline/Close-Grip Press
   b. Pin Press No Straight Weight All Bands
   c. Behind Head Tricep Extensions on Cable Machine
   d. Plate Raises
   e. Bent-Over Dumbbell Row
   f. Body Weight Pushups and Tricep Extensions, Both to Failure

9. **Option Nine**
   a. Z Press Seated on the Floor
   b. Isometric Pin Presses in Flat Bench
   c. Dumbbell Roll-Backs Decline Bench
   d. Hammer Strength Machine Press
   e. Plate Raises
   f. Lat Pull-Down (Use different grip than previous)

10. **Option Ten**
    a. Floor Press with Monster Minis
    b. Heavy Dumbbell Presses Flat Bench
    c. JM Presses with Football Bar
    d. Bradford Press
    e. Face Pulls off Cable Machine
    f. Tricep Push-Downs to Failure
    g. Elevated Weighted Push-Ups to Failure

11. **Option Eleven**
    a. Incline Press with Football Bar
    b. Hanging Dumbbell Presses
    c. Power Clean
    d. Plate Raises
    e. Pec Dec Fly
    f. Dumbbell Snatches (Ultra-high reps)
    g. Wheelbarrow Shrugs

12. **Option Twelve**
    a. Flat Bench with Average Bands
    b. Pin Press
    c. EZ Bar Skull Crushers
    d. Incline Dumbbell Press
    e. JM Press off of a Pin with Lighter Weight
    f. Push-Ups to Failure

13. **Option Thirteen**
    a. Decline Bench with Football Bar
    b. Decline JM Press with Football Bar
    c. Chest-Supported Rows
    d. One-Arm Dumbbell Press
    e. Light Dumbbell Rollbacks Superset with Banded Pushdowns
    f. Push-Ups to Failure

14. **Option Fourteen**
    a. Pin Press Straight Weight for a Max
    b. Dumbbell Rollbacks (Heavy)
    c. Seated Bradford Press
    d. Lat Pull-Down (Change the attachment from last time)
    e. Face Pulls with Cable

15. **Option Fifteen**
    a. Flat Bench
    b. Heavy Dumbbell Rollbacks
    c. Row on Hammer Strength Machine
    d. Standing OHP
    e. Pec Dec Fly
    f. T-Bar Row
    g. Push-Ups to Failure

As you can see by the listed M-E workouts, there are many optional workouts to rotate. Using different amounts of chains and four other band tensions enlarges the options. A combo of chains and bands can also be used. Every three or four weeks, a large volume of dumbbells can be used instead of a barbell. You can get a record with a close, medium, or wide grip on pressing exercises. Only do the workouts and special exercises that work for you. It does no good to be strong in the wrong exercises.

OLYMPIC WEIGHTLIFTING

The theory of Westside Barbell training is the same as the Chinese use with their own Olympic-style lifts. Below is a list of 15 M-E workouts to rotate each exercise day. You can mix jerks and jerk training with clean and snatch training. Of course, the squat must also be increased, going as heavy as possible on one workout for M-E work.

A barbell lift is always first, and then three or four small special exercises afterward. Don't forget your GPP with short rest intervals for part of your GPP. Along with treadmill work, weight sled, pushups, pullups, Dips, Belt Squats, and Reverse Hypers TM. This is just a small part of the Chinese training to correct a weak muscle group.

SPECIAL NOTE: It is the author's view that Olympic weight training is very minimal, and this is keeping them from excelling worldwide. Weak backs and legs are the problems.

M-E Olympic Lifting Workouts

1. **Power Clean from Floor**
   a. Back Raise
   b. High Pull Clean Grip
   c. Arched Back Goodmorning
   d. Reverse Hyper

2. **Front Squat Plus Jerk**
   a. High Pull
   b. Arched Back Goodmorning
   c. Back Raise
   d. Reverse Hyper

3. **Clean Pull with Four Stops Upward**
   a. Belt Squat
   b. Belt Squat Power Clean
   c. Calf-Ham-Glute Raise
   d. Reverse Hyper

4. **Clean Pull at Knees**
   a. Belt Squat
   b. Back Raise
   c. Arched Back Goodmorning
   d. Box Jumps, 40 Total

5. **Band Squat with 250 Pounds of Tension Plus Barbell Weight**
   a. Power Snatch
   b. Upright Rows
   c. Back Raise
   d. Box Jumps, 40 Total

6. **Concentric Snatch off Boxes**
   a. Front Squat
   b. Calf-Ham-Glute Raise
   c. Overhead Squat with Snatch Grip
   d. Pull Weight Sled

7. **Clean Standing on Box**
   a. Front Squat
   b. Back Raise
   c. Snatch-Grip Deadlift
   d. Calf-Glute-Ham Raise

8. **Clean Pull-Off from Floor**
   a. Belt Squat
   b. Upright Row
   c. Isometric Pull, Two Positions
   d. Box Jumps

9. **Jerk Barbell Behind Head**
   a. Push Press
   b. Goodmorning Legs Straight
   c. Back Raise
   d. Reverse Hyper]

10. **Squat with Jerk Behind Head**
    a. Press Behind the Head, Snatch Grip
    b. Depth Jump
    c. Incline Press
    d. Back Raise

11. **Power Snatch, Legs Straight, Torse Leaning Over**
    a. Close-Grip Snatch
    b. Back Raise
    c. Barbell Lunge Bar on Back
    d. Walk with Bar on Chest from Rack to Rack

12. **Snatch Pull Standing on Block**
    a. Front Squat
    b. Belt Squat
    c. Upright Row
    d. Bend-Over Row

13. **Power Snatch then Overhead Squat**
    a. Back Squat
    b. Calf-Ham-Glute Raise
    c. Leg Press
    d. Depth Jump

14. **Clean Pull to Knee, then Full Clean Pull**
    a. Goodmorning Seated on Bench
    b. Lunge wi8th Barbell on Chest
    c. Back Raise
    d. Reverse Hyper

15. **Clean and Jerk from Floor**
    a. High Pu7ll Clean Grip
    b. Belt Squat Power Clean
    c. Back Raise
    d. Reverse Hyper

The above programs can be implemented in any order you wish. Medvedev has many more M-E workouts to choose from in *Supertraining* or *Fundamentals of Special Strength Training in Sport*.

This came from the experiments at the world-famous Dynamo Club in the former Soviet Union in 1972. Seventy high-skilled weightlifters were instructed to use 24 to 40 special exercises for 12 weeks, and then the lifters' feedback and remarks were examined. One lifter was satisfied, but the rest wanted more special exercises, both small and large.

I am amazed how many Olympic lifters ask if they can use the Conjugate System when it was first implemented by Olympic weightlifters at the before-mentioned Dynamo Club. Y. V. Verkhoshansky was also heavily involved with the Conjugate System for Track and Field. Remember, it is not just large and small special exercises and the classical lifts to be rotated, but also volume, intensity, rest intervals, velocities, GPP, and restoration methods.

"Many things have changed, but the effort has not, and never will."
—Louie Simmons

CONJUGATE FOR TRACK AND FIELD

Y. V. Verkhoshansky had a significant influence on introducing the Conjugate System to Track and Field in 1972, which was the same time the system was being used for Olympic lifters at the Dynamo Club.

To use the Conjugate System for Track and Field today, first, stop using Block Periodization. Instead, use a three-week wave periodization plan when only functional training can be evaluated daily.

Typically, there are four periods of training. The Accumulation Period will introduce the athlete to a high volume of work with moderate intensity or speed during all exercises and movements. The heart rate should be kept at 150 to 160 beats per minute. The training mostly will be GPP that closely resembles SPP, but also it will restart the training process for the next upcoming competition. It will coordinate light exercises along with some technical activities and local strength endurance work. Basically, it covers most aspects of GPP.

The Accumulation Period usually takes place every year to start training for Track and Field. But Westside only runs an Accumulation Phase one time because Westside does not have an off-season. The athletes train year-round. Why climb up the mountain halfway only to go back down and start again? Westside combines the Intensification and Transformation Phases during the general preparatory and special preparatory phases to correspond with the competition period. This is accomplished by utilizing the Conjugate System.

Whatever is needed at the present time is introduced into training to fulfill a physical or technical void. Sprinters and longer-distance runners are constantly overtraining. Westside found this happens, making Maximum Effort on the track and in the weight room at the same time. It is simply too much and causes too many injuries. The total workload should include a small amount of technical work on the track—roughly 20 percent. The other 80 percent is for building strength, such as Strength Endurance, and working on single-joint special exercises.

Let's look at a 15-workout program that will build maximum strength and explosive power through jumping.

- We vary intensity weekly to avoid accommodation to these exercises.

- We use three-week waves for the main exercises. We constantly vary band tension for the treadmill, weights for the weight vest, and different times.

- It is essential to count steps on the treadmill for progress.

- We change the primary exercises after three weeks. For example, we implement front squats after a three-week wave of back squats.

- To avoid psychological burnout, once we stop making progress in the jumps or on the treadmill, we switch exercises entirely.

- The activities mentioned above are a mainstay in a particular athlete's training, but you must identify your athlete's weaknesses and adjust accordingly.

- Remember, 80 percent for accessories and 20 percent for main exercises go for track athletes as well!

Week #1 Monday

- Speed Squat (standing in foam) 5x5 @ 75 Percent
- 25 Drop Jumps for Max Height, 55 Inches
- 10 Seconds Non-Motorized Treadmill, Bands Around Hips and Ankles
- GHD Machine, Four to Six Reps, 45 pounds
- Hypers, Abs
- Calf Jumps in Plyo Swing

Week #1 Thursday

- Hatfield Squat 5x5 @ 80 percent
- 10 Seconds Non-Motorized Treadmill with Weight Vest
- MR-19
- Inverse Curl
- 25 Depth Jumps for Max Height, 57 Inches
- K Box
- Hypers, Abs, Calf Jumps in Plyo Swing

Week #2 Monday

- Speed Squat (standing in foam) 5x5 @ 85 Percent
- Depth Jumps
- 12 Seconds Non-Motorized Treadmill, Bands Around Hips and Ankles
- Heavy Step-Ups to a High Box
- GHD Machine, Add Weight
- Hypers, Abs, Calf Jumps in Plyo Swing

Week #2 Thursday

- Hatfield Squat 5x5 @ 85 Percent
- 12 Seconds Non-Motorized Treadmill with Weight Vest
- MR-19
- Belt Squat Jumps
- Inverse Curl
- Hypers, Abs, Calf Jumps in Plyo Swig

Week #3 Monday

- Speed Squat (Standing in Foam) 5x5 @ 90 percent
- Depth Jumps—Jump Up Tough 9'4"
- 15 Seconds Non-Motorized Treadmill Bands Around Hips and Ankles
- 45 Degrees GHD Extension
- Sled Pulls for Time
- Hypers, Abs, Calf Jumps in Plyo Swing

Week #3 Thursday

- Hatfield Squat 5x5 @ 90 percent
- 15 Seconds Non-Motorized Treadmill with Weight Vest
- MR-19
- Low Belt Squats
- Depth Jumps
- GHD with Weight
- Hypers, Abs

Week #4 Monday

- Depth Jumps, 25 Jumps
- Front Squat 5x5 Reps @ 75 percent
- Calf-Ham-Glute
- K-Box Eccentric Work
- Plyo Swing
- Reverse Hyper Static Holds, 3x5 Sets @ 80 Pounds

Week #4 Thursday

- Hatfield Squat 5x5 Reps, 5x5 @ 75 Percent
- Drop Jumps 6 to 5 Inch, 5x5 Drops
- Inverse Curl
- 10 Seconds Non-Motorized Treadmill, four trips
- Plyo Swing
- Reverse Hyper Static Holds, 5x5 Holds @ 85 percent

Week #5 Monday

- Depth Jumps Off 20-Inch Box, 5x5 Jumps
- Front Squat 5x5 Reps @ 80 Percent
- 45 Percent Back Raise with Weight
- K-Box
- Powerwalk Sled Work, Six Trips, 60 Meters
- Calf Jumps on Plyo Swing
- MR-19

Week #5 Thursday

- Depth Jumps Off 58-Inch Box, 5x5 Drops
- Front Squat 5x5 Reps @ 85 percent
- K-Box
- Step-Ups on 30-Inch Box 8 kg Kettlebells
- Reverse Hypers

Week #6 Monday

- Wide Sumo Deadlift 5x5 Reps
- Low Box Belt Squat 5x5 Reps
- Calf-Ham-Glute Raises
- Depth Jump Off 20-Inch Box, 5x5 Jumps
- Reverse Hypers 70-Pound Static Holds

Week #7 Thursday

- Wide Sumo Deadlift on Two-Inch Box 5x5 Reps
- Low-Box Belt Squat 5x5 Reps
- MR-19
- Standing Leg Curl

Week #8 Monday

- Power Clean 5x5 Reps
- Plyo Swing Jumps 5x10 Reps
- 45 Percent Back Raise
- Inverse Curl
- Reverse Hypers

Week #9 Thursday

- Drop Jumps 60-Inch Box 4x5 Reps
- Front Squat 5x5 Reps @ 75 Percent
- Calf-Ham-Glute Raises
- Power Walking with Weight Sled, 10 Trips
- Inverse Curl

Week #10 Monday

- Front Squat 5x5 Reps @ 80 Percent
- Wide Sumo Deadlift 5x5 Reps
- Inverse Curl
- 45 Percent Back Raise
- Power Weight Sled Walks, Eight Trips, 60 Meters

The workouts above are samples of the many Westside uses during the year. When performing a power clean or power snatch, Squat, Press, or Deadlift, use a three-week wave starting at 75 percent, then 80 percent the second week, then 85 percent on the third week. Lift 5x5 reps for Speed-Strength.

If you switch to a second barbell lift, start at 75 percent for the first week for building restoration. As you can see, the volume will increase five percent on weeks two and three. Then, it drops 10 percent to start the next pendulum wave.

Jumps of all kinds should start low and go up for the next two weeks as well. Then, rotate to one of three—depth jumps, drop jumps, or box jumps. When box jumping, rotate from ankle weights, weight vest, or Kettlebells.

There will be six to eight small workouts for what muscles may be lagging behind during the weekly plan.

Most of the running is on a non-motorized treadmill or power walking with a heavyweight sled or sprinting in the grass with 25 pounds (women) or 45 pounds (men) on the sled. The grass is much safer for most sprinting and sprint work.

Don't forget to add upper-body work as well. The upper body must be strong to maintain proper running technique with perfect posture.

A 100- or 200-meter sprinter would do resistance sled work for 40 and 60 meters with four- or five-minutes rest between runs for a total of 300 to 350 total meters. For Acceleration Training, use 10 to 30 meters with a six-minute average rest interval.

To build up your speed, do 3x10-meter flys with six-minute rest periods. Plus, 2x120-meter runs with six to eight minutes recovery. This is a full rotation of distance. It could be 5x15 meters two-point starts with a 25- to 45-pound sled or 5x20 meters with a vest weighing 10 percent of the sprinter's bodyweight.

A proven method by Westside done first by Glen Mills is to sprint for three to seven seconds and measure the distance you cover. Set a marker and try to increase the distance on each preceding run. This will show an increase in your acceleration phase. The three to seven seconds should translate to 30 to 60 meters. When using 40 seconds, it will show an increase in the top speed maintenance phase. No more the 400 meters total.

Track all records for everything. Box Jumping both depth jumps and drop jumps as well as box jumps. And all distances and times to cover the distance.

Let's look at four more gym workouts to use or mix and match in any way that suits your needs.

Gym Workout One

- Snatch-Grip Deadlift
- March in Belt Squat with Wide Stance, Two Minutes
- Power Clean
- Overhead Press
- Reverse Hypers

Gym Workout Two

- 5x50 Meter Sprint with Three-Pound Weight
- Jumps in Place
- Plyo Swing Jumps
- Calf-Ham-Glute Raise
- Reverse Hypers

Gym Workout Three

- Sumo Deadlift for Max, One Rep
- Weighted Box Jumps for Maximum Height
- Glute Bridge with Barbell
- Plyo Push-Ups
- Chin-Ups

Gym Workout Four

- Low Box Squat in Belt Squat for Max, Five Reps
- Hip Ab Machine
- Single-Leg K-Box Squats
- K-Box Reverse Hypers
- Squat Jumps in Static Dynamic Developer

The workouts are endless; just pick the work you need at the present time. Remember, special strength is measured in velocity, not weight.

You may have noticed that many of the workouts finish with the Reverse Hyper TM. The Reverse Hyper machine will build massive strength but also is an unparalleled traction device. Needless lower-body injuries happen due to too much running and lowering your base of GPP as the season progresses. Using a Reverse Hyper machine throughout the season helps to prevent these injuries.

The Conjugate System switches and rotates all manner of training. You'll see the variation in all weight exercises, volume, intensities, velocities, rest intervals, length of a workout, and restoration. The system includes cardio devices like bikes, rowing machines, ski machines, and treadmills with and without a motor. It even varies your nutrition.

When a runner is on the track, their methods and distances must change to avoid the Speed Barrier. Once a runner constantly repeats the same distance at the same speed, they then find they are unable to make further gains. At that point, the athlete must stop running and replace it with jumping, bounding, and weight training. This is very common for ballplayers.

Even the outfits you wear while training can make a difference in your success. Emmanuel Stuart of the world-famous Kronk Boxing Gym in Detroit trained the world heavyweight boxing champ W. W. Klitschko, a slow-footed fighter who wore black boxing shoes. Stuart had him wear red shoes to feel he was faster on his feet, but more importantly, it made his rivals think he was faster. The body constantly changes, and so must training. Otherwise, the dreaded biological Law of Accommodation will undoubtedly destroy your training programs.

REFERENCES

Kurz, Thomas, *Science of Sports Training*, Island Pont, Vermont: Stadion, 1990.

The World Atlas of Exercises for Track and Field

Andrzej Lasocki

Laputin, N. P. and V. G. Oleshko, *Managing the Training of Weightlifters*, Livonia, Michigan: Sportivny Press, 1989.

Ross, Barry, *Underground Secrets to Faster Running*, Lexington, Kentucky: Bear Powered Publishing, 2005

Siff, Mel C., Ph.D., *Supertraining,* Denver, Colorado: Supertraining Institute, 2004

Simmons, Louie, *Book of Methods*, Westside Barbell, 2007

Simmons, Louie, *Bench Press Manual,* Westside4Athletes, 2009

Simmons, Louie, *Explosive Strength Development for Jumping,* Westside4Athletes, 2014

Simmons, Louie, *Special Strength Development for All Sports,* Westside4Athletes, 2015

Simmons, Louie, *Squat and Deadlift Manual,* Westside4Athletes, 2011

Simmons, Louie, *Strength Manual for Running,* Westside4Athletes, 2017

Starzynski, Tadeusz, and Henryk Sozanski, *Explosive Power and Jumping Ability for All Sports*, Island Pond, Vermont: Stadium Publishing, 1995.

Y.V. Verkhoshansky, Yuri V., Fundamentals of Special Strength Training in Sport, Livonia, Michigan: Sportivny Press, 1997.

Verkhoshansky, Yuri, Shock Method, Translation by Natalia Verkhoshansky, Verkhoshansky SSTM©: Rome, Italy, 2018.

V.M. Zatsiorsky, V. M., and W. J. Kraemer, *Science and Practice of Strength Training,* Champaign, Illinois: Human Kinetics, 1995.

Made in the USA
Columbia, SC
31 December 2022

74296353R10070